Solid-State Circuits
for
Hobbyists & Experimenters

by
Jon L. Turino

HOWARD W. SAMS & CO., INC.
THE BOBBS-MERRILL CO., INC.
INDIANAPOLIS · KANSAS CITY · NEW YORK

Preface

This book is designed to provide the serious electronics hobbyist or experimenter with enough information to allow him to design the circuitry for a great many useful projects. Also, it should supply him with enough knowledge to be able to adapt and modify existing circuit designs to suit his specific purposes.

It is a practical book—without reference to semiconductor physics or manufacturing processes. Since the "hole and electron" transistor theory is available in a large number of technical publications, it is not repeated herein.

The first chapter is of paramount importance, covering in detail the creation of a system block diagram. The second chapter is a review of practical semiconductor device theory and includes descriptions of bias polarities for each device. Also included in this chapter are terminal identification drawings. Following this, single- and multiple-stage analog amplifiers are developed and later used as signal sources and detectors. Special purpose circuits and digital logic are also discussed, followed by a chapter on the use of analog ICs. The concluding chapter describes the design of several types of power supplies.

It is the intention of this book to show the "why," in addition to the "how to," of solid-state circuit design, so that the reader will be able to use this material as a foundation for further growth and development. There are only a few prerequisites for making the best use of this book—a knowledge of basic electronics, the desire to do creative design, and imagination. Armed with these tools, your study of solid-state circuit design should prove both instructive and enjoyable.

JON L. TURINO

Contents

CHAPTER 1

System Design by Block Diagram

The design of any electronic system begins with an idea. But what happens subsequent to the idea is what determines how well (or even if) the system will function. If the idea is converted to circuitry in a planned, logical fashion, rather than haphazardly, the chances that the system will function are considerably improved.

There are as many methods for converting ideas to circuitry as there are people who design circuits. The method described in this chapter is one of the better methods, since it provides for converting systems to circuits by means of an orderly approach that may be acquired by learning (instead of requiring an inherited creative genius).

Before details of each step are discussed, an overview of this design approach will prove helpful. There are four operations to be performed in order to convert an idea to circuitry. These are:

1. *DEFINE* the system. What must it do? At this step the idea is defined in terms of the output response required from the system when a given input stimulus is provided.
2. *CREATE* the block diagram. This step involves breaking the system block into smaller, easier-to-handle functional blocks. Each of these smaller blocks is then defined in terms of input stimulus/output response.

3. *CONVERT* the blocks to circuit functions. This involves translating the input/output characteristics of a block to the input/output characteristics of a specific circuit type (oscillator, amplifier, etc.), which will be designed to perform in the exact manner required.
4. *ANALYZE* the tentative design to determine whether it will, in fact, provide the output response defined in the first step when its input is stimulated. During this step it may be necessary to go back into Step 2 (or 3) and refine the design until it appears to function properly.

This four-step method is shown graphically with the flow chart in Fig. 1-1. Of particular importance are the feedback lines from "Analysis" to "Creation" and "Analysis" to "Conversion." If the first attempt at creating a workable design is not completely satisfactory, the design should be modified before actual circuit design begins. The reason for this is that it is easier at this point to determine whether the design or an

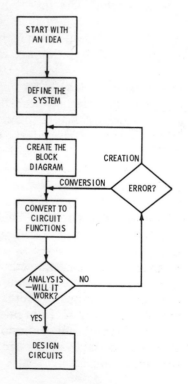

Fig. 1-1. System design flow chart.

individual stage is at fault, if the system fails to function properly.

DEFINE THE SYSTEM OPERATION

The first step in practical solid-state design is to define the system operation required for the idea to function. In this first step, the system is treated as a "black box," and its function is defined in terms of the input and output requirements. This may involve more than one set of stimulus/response definitions for the black box, as shown in the exaggerated example of the doorbell in Fig. 1-2. Regardless of the simplicity or complexity of the final system design, it all starts right here. What does the system have to do? This is the operative question.

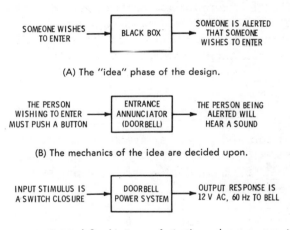

(A) The "idea" phase of the design.

(B) The mechanics of the idea are decided upon.

(C) The system operation is defined in terms of stimulus and response requirements.

Fig. 1-2. The evolution of an idea.

Several other systems and some different methods of listing the input and output stimuli are shown in Figs. 1-3, 1-4, 1-5, and 1-6. These examples are intended to show how the system should be defined so that the system block diagram can be created and proper circuitry can be designed.

The input stimulus must be identified so that the input interface of the system will be able to accommodate it. It is necessary to specify, in electrical terms, the type of input signal to be applied and the differences that must be detected in it for a given output response. Then the input device(s) must be

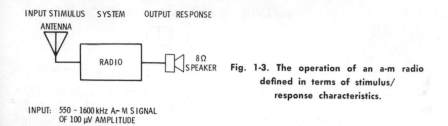

Fig. 1-3. The operation of an a-m radio defined in terms of stimulus/response characteristics.

chosen to provide the system input with those electrical characteristics.

The output response must match the response of the output device being used if the system is to operate properly. Regardless of whether the input and output devices, or the input and

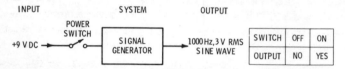

Fig. 1-4. Signal generator with input stimulus provided by switch closure.

output stimuli and responses are specified first, they must be compatible with each other. Only when this interface requirement is met will the definition of the input and output of the system be accurate.

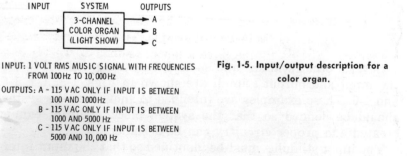

Fig. 1-5. Input/output description for a color organ.

CREATE THE BLOCK DIAGRAM

Once the system operation has been defined, the next step is to develop a block diagram with input and output stages that

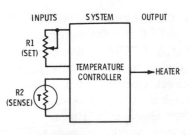

INPUTS   SYSTEM   OUTPUT

Fig. 1-6. Multiple-input circuit requiring
two input/output definitions.

INPUTS: 1 - TEMP SETTING
           2 - TEMP SENSING

OUTPUT: 115 V AC IF TEMP SETTING IS GREATER THAN
           TEMP SENSING

INPUTS: TEMP SETTING - VARIABLE RESISTANCE
                          FROM 0 - 10,000 Ω
           TEMP SENSING - VARIABLE RESISTANCE
                          FROM 1000 - 10,000 Ω

OUTPUT: 115 V AC IF R1 > R2

are compatible with the system requirements. Also, the diagram should have intervening stages that perform the functions necessary to make the output respond properly when the input is stimulated.

This step is the truly creative part of design, and a healthy amount of imagination is a valuable asset. Remember that there is no reason why something can *not* be done. Everything *can* be done, even if it does take forever! Allow your mind to roam and experiment with new and different approaches to the problem of creating the block diagram. Look at design as a challenge to be met head-on and conquered. If it turns out that the system will not function as diagrammed, revise or refine it until it does function.

One important goal that should be considered as you create a block diagram is this: keep it simple. This goal is extremely important. Simple things have a better chance of working the first time, are more reliable, and are less expensive than complex gadgetry.

Where do you start to create a system block diagram? The answer, of course, is to start with the information that is known—namely the input and output. These two stages should be drawn first, and their operation should be defined in the same terms as the system was defined. The object of starting at opposite ends of the system and working toward the center is to make the stages converge. This means that we must find a stage in the center whose input is compatible with the output of the previous stage, and whose output is compatible with the input of the following stage. An example of this is shown in Fig. 1-7. The convergence stage need not be the stage that is exactly in the middle of a design—it could be either of the stages marked with a dagger (†), depending on whether the block diagram was started at the left or the right. The point is that there *is* a stage in the system that ties everything together; working from both ends to the middle is one good way to complete a design.

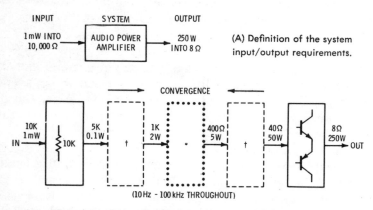

(A) Definition of the system input/output requirements.

(B) Stage marked with asterisk ties input and output together.

Fig. 1-7. Creating a system block diagram for an audio power amplifier.

As each stage is added to the block diagram, its input and output requirements should be noted. These requirements should be at least as detailed as the system input/output requirements (including such things as voltage, frequency, and impedance), since these stages must eventually become circuits.

Figs. 1-8, 1-9, 1-10, and 1-11 show the block diagrams of the four systems that were defined in Figs. 1-3, 1-4, 1-5, and 1-6 to illustrate system definition requirements. The numbers above the stages represent the order in which they were decided upon (and are, for the most part, arbitrarily assigned). The stage that could be considered the most likely "convergence" stage is marked with an asterisk (*). In Fig. 1-8, the rf-amplifier and output-amplifier stages (1) are done first since their interface characteristics are known. The oscillator-mixer stage (2) is used to make the signal easier to handle when it is amplified by the i-f amplifier stage (3). The detector stage (*) is

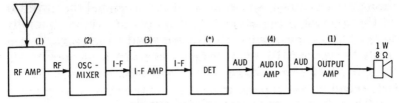

Fig. 1-8. Block diagram of an a-m radio.

marked as the convergence stage, since it bridges the gap between the modulated rf and the demodulated audio. However, the audio-amplifier stage (4) could be construed as the stage that ties the detector audio to the output amplifier. (This distinction depends on the designer's point of view.) In Fig. 1-9, the input, output, and convergence stages are one and the same, since the specified output can be generated by a one-stage circuit.

Fig. 1-9. Block diagram of a one-stage
signal generator.

The convergence stage in Fig. 1-10 is the rectifier-amplifier stage (*) if you use the following reasoning: The ac control stage (1) is done first since it is the output stage. It will control the ac output signal when a dc voltage is applied to its input. The filter stage (2) is done next since the input needs to be split three ways. The next and last requirement is to make

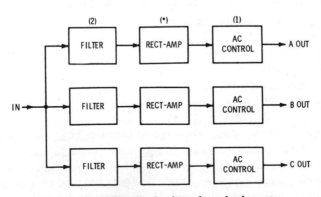

Fig. 1-10. Block diagram of a three-channel color organ.

the ac signal from the filter stage into a dc signal that will turn on the ac control stage. This is done in the rectifier-amplifier stage. In Fig. 1-11, the convergence point of the circuit is actually the connection between the first and second stages, since the output of the first stage is compatible with the input of the second stage.

Although starting at the ends and working toward the middle is one good way of creating a working block diagram, it is by no means the only way, nor is it always the most efficient. If you already have a good idea of what stages will be required to change an input stimulus to an output response, there is no reason to alter that idea, unless an analysis shows it to be unworkable. The important thing is to create a block diagram that can be converted to circuit functions, analyzed, and refined to the point where it will work.

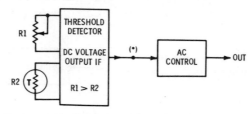

Fig. 1-11. Block diagram of a simple temperature controller.

CONVERT THE BLOCKS TO CIRCUIT FUNCTIONS

By the time the block diagram has been completed and the inputs and outputs of each stage identified, putting names on the circuits is a comparatively easy task. Most circuits will fall into one of four major categories:

1. Amplifiers—ac and/or dc.
2. Signal sources.
3. Signal detectors.
4. Control circuits.

There are many special-purpose circuits that do not fit into any of these categories, however, and these circuits must be given names and be designed to perform the proper functions. With a thorough knowledge of the features and characteristics of today's solid-state devices, it should not be too difficult to select the best device for a specific application and design a working circuit around it.

The input and output characteristics of several circuits, along with the devices that may be used most effectively to achieve the desired circuit results, are discussed in Table 1-1.

ANALYZE THE DESIGN

After the block diagram has been created and converted to circuit functions, all that remains (except for the actual circuit design and checkout) is the analysis of the design to ensure that it will indeed function when it is constructed. This is not to say that modifications will not have to be made on the bench. Very few circuits, let alone complete projects, function perfectly without some adjustments to component values, interconnections, etc. The purpose of the analysis of the design is to catch gross errors in signal flow and circuit functions.

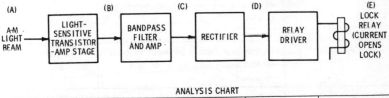

Fig. 1-12. Example of steps to be taken in analyzing a system design.

Possibly the best approach in analyzing a new design is to apply the input stimulus mentally through the system to the output. The effects of input stimulus should be examined for each of the possible input states and for all inputs, in several combinations. The input and output of each stage in the system should be examined.

An example of the steps that should be taken when a design is being analyzed is shown in Fig. 1-12. The design is for a modulated, light-sensitive, lock-opening receiver. This circuit is relatively simple to analyze, since it has only three possible input states on one input and has a straight-through path from input to output.

Table 1-1. Circuit Names, Input/Output Characteristics, and Recommended Devices

Circuit	Input/Output Characteristics	Devices
Active Filter	Analog amplifier with frequency-selective feedback. Output size (and sometimes shape) varies with changes in input frequency.	FET, Bipolar Transistor
Amplifier	Output is a replica (in-phase or out-of-phase) of the input signal. The FET is for low-power application. Many configurations usable for a large number of applications.	FET, Bipolar Transistor
Constant-Current Source	Maintains a constant current through it over wide range of voltages across it.	Bipolar Transistor, FET, Field-Effect Diode
Detector	Output is proportional to the variations of a modulated signal.	Diode, Bipolar Transistor
Flip-Flop	Output changes state (and remains) each time the input is activated or pulsed.	Bipolar Transistor
Gated Amplifier	Output is a replica of input when a second input (usually a dc level) is provided.	FET, Bipolar Transistor
Mixer	Output contains the sum and difference (plus originals) of two different frequencies.	FET, Bipolar Transistor, Diode
One-Shot Multivibrator	Output is a pulse of variable width and occurs each time the input is activated.	Bipolar Transistor
Relay Driver	Allows current to flow in relay coil in response to a change in input voltage.	FET, Bipolar Transistor, SCR, Triac
Sawtooth Oscillator	The dc voltage supplied results in a sawtooth (exponential or linear) output waveform whose frequency, amplitude, and linearity can be controlled.	UJT, PUT, Four-Layer Diode, FET, Field-Effect Diode
Sine-Wave Oscillator	The dc voltage supplied results in a sinusoidal output whose amplitude and frequency can be controlled.	FET, Bipolar Transistor
Summing Amplifier	Output is the sum (or combination) of the input signals.	Bipolar Transistor, FET

Table 1-1. Circuit Names, Input/Output Characteristics,
and Recommended Devices (Cont)

Circuit	Input/Output Characteristics	Devices
Threshold Detector	Output changes (usually radically) when the input level goes above or below a preset limit.	FET, Bipolar Transistor, UJT, PUT, Four-Layer Diode
Voltage-Controlled Oscillator	Output frequency changes with changes in input voltage.	Bipolar transistor, FET, UJT, PUT

SUMMARY

To summarize this chapter, it is important to keep in mind the four basic steps in electronic system design—*define, create, convert,* and *analyze.* If your first attempts are not satisfactory, go back and *re*-create or *re*-convert until the *analysis* shows that the circuit should work. This approach can also be used to modify an existing project design if that appears to be a better way to get a working model than starting from scratch. Avoid "reinventing the wheel" wherever you can.

Now that you are equipped with a knowledge of how to design a new project from an idea, it is time to look at the devices that will do the actual work.

CHAPTER 2

Practical Diode and Transistor Theory

Modern circuit design is based on the use of semiconductor devices such as diodes and transistors. This chapter discusses the characteristics of these devices that must be understood before the design procedures in subsequent chapters can be put to use.

DIODES

The semiconductor diode, in its many and varied forms, is one of the basic building blocks in any circuit design. Rectifier diodes are used to provide dc voltages to operate the functioning circuitry in a system. Small-signal diodes are used for signal steering, control, low-level rectification, and many other miscellaneous functions. The zener (or reverse-breakdown) diode plays an important role in the design of power supplies and is discussed later in this chapter.

The schematic symbol for the rectifier and small-signal diode is shown in Fig. 2-1, along with sketches of several types of diodes and package styles. There are many more packaging configurations than are shown here, but the examples are representative of most of them. Note particularly the "reverse-polarity" type. If the terminal identity is questionable, it may be pinned down by the method described later in this text. The polarity of the voltage applied across the two terminals—anode and cathode—determines the characteristics the device will display.

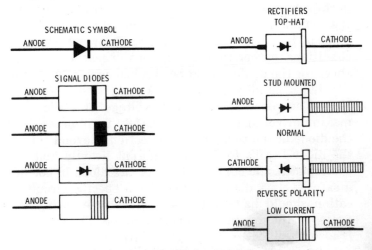

Fig. 2-1. Diode schematic symbol and several package styles.

Diode Characteristics

There are two modes of operation for the diode—conducting and nonconducting. The diode will allow current to flow in one direction only; it is an "open circuit" in the other direction (except for certain leakage currents, to be discussed later.) The diode will conduct, or allow electrons to flow, when it is "forward biased" by a potential applied across it. Fig. 2-2 depicts the polarity and characteristics for both forward (conducting) and reverse (nonconducting) bias conditions. The forward voltage values shown are typical for silicon diodes. The forward voltage drop for diodes made of germanium is considerably less, on the order of 0.2 to 0.35 volt.

When a diode is used in a circuit, there are four characteristics that are important. These are:

1. V_F— The forward voltage drop across the diode when it is conducting a specified current. This value will vary, depending on the current through the diode, and this variation must be taken into account when circuitry is designed.

2. $I_{F(max)}$—The maximum forward current that can safely be passed through the diode when it is conducting. If this value is exceeded, the diode may be destroyed. It is important to use a diode whose $I_{F(max)}$ rating is higher than the maximum current expected to flow through it. The value of $I_{F(max)}$ is sometimes specified for pulsed operating conditions, rather than continuous operation, so the data sheet for the diode should be checked carefully. The quantity $I_{F(max)}$ is also specified as $I_{O(max)}$.

3. V_{BR}—The reverse breakdown voltage of a diode is the maximum voltage which may safely be impressed across the diode in the reverse bias direction. Beyond this value, the diode begins to conduct current heavily and will be destroyed if the current through the diode is not held to a safe level. A diode selected for a specific circuit application should have a breakdown voltage rating well in excess of the maximum expected value. The quantity V_{BR} is also specified as PIV (peak inverse voltage) or PRV (peak reverse voltage).

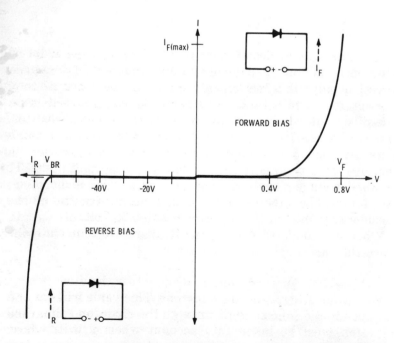

Fig. 2-2. A diode characteristic curve.

4. I_R—The reverse current is the leakage current through the diode when it is reverse biased and is usually specified at or near the V_{BR} value of reverse bias. The leakage current through most silicon signal diodes is usually small enough to be ignored in a circuit design, although its value should be checked to ensure that it will not affect circuit operation. Leakage can be significant in sensitive low-level circuits.

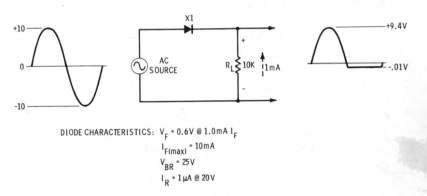

DIODE CHARACTERISTICS: $V_F = 0.6V$ @ $1.0mA$ I_F
$I_{F(max)} = 10mA$
$V_{BR} = 25V$
$I_R = 1\mu A$ @ $20V$

Fig. 2-3. A simple diode circuit.

The simple circuit shown in Fig. 2-3 illustrates the effect of each of the four diode parameters just discussed. The diode characteristics that affect circuit operation are listed as they may be found on data sheets or on parts packages. Note that we have 9.4 V, rather than 10 V, developed across the load resistor, due to the drop across the diode. The forward current through the circuit is 1 mA and $I_{F(max)}$ is specified as 10 mA, so there is no danger of destroying the diode. The V_{BR} of diode X1 is 25 V, and since there is only 10 V across it in the reverse direction, there is no danger. Note that due to I_R, some portion of the negative-going waveform is present across R_L. In this circuit, the .01 V is quite negligible. It is shown to demonstrate the fact that it exists.

Diode Testing

Fig. 2-4 illustrates the use of an ohmmeter or a battery and an ammeter to identify the anode and cathode on unmarked diodes. The same methods are also used to test a diode whose operational status is in doubt. When using an ohmmeter to test diodes, set it to the R × 1000 or R × 10,000 range rather than R × 1, to avoid damaging the diode. Most ohmmeters will supply a large amount of current on the low range. The ohmmeter illustrated in Fig. 2-4A is typical of most VOM's. When the instrument is set to an ohms range, the red lead is usually connected to the negative (−) side of the internal battery, instead of being the positive connection. The polarity of any VOM can be checked by measuring a known good diode or measuring the VOM with another voltmeter.

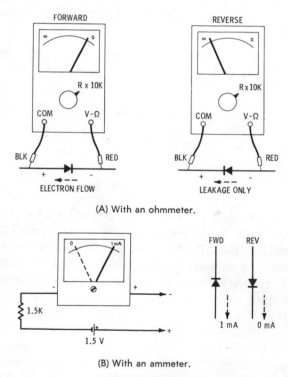

(A) With an ohmmeter.

(B) With an ammeter.

Fig. 2-4. Diode testing.

The ratio of back-to-front resistance for a good diode should be at least 1000 to 1. When checking a diode that is installed in a circuit, take into account any current paths through components connected to the device. The 1000-to-1 ratio may not hold. It is sufficient to obtain a 10-to-1 difference in most circuits. If in doubt, disconnect one end of the diode to isolate it and then perform the test.

BIPOLAR TRANSISTORS

The bipolar transistor comes in many sizes, shapes, and varieties, as illustrated in Fig. 2-5. There are two types of bipolar devices—npn and pnp. They function in an identical fashion except that the polarity of the voltage applied to pnp transistors is exactly opposite to that applied to npn devices.

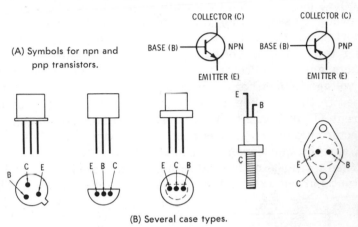

(A) Symbols for npn and pnp transistors.

(B) Several case types.

Fig. 2-5. Bipolar transistors.

The npn transistor is used most frequently throughout this text for illustrating design steps. If the polarities of supply voltages, electrolytic capacitors, and diodes are reversed, any npn transistor may be replaced by an electrically similar pnp transistor. Many circuits use both types of transistors, taking advantage of the flexibility this method allows.

Bipolar Transistor Characteristics

Where semiconductor diodes have two modes of operation, the bipolar transistor has three—cutoff, saturated, and active. In the cutoff mode (or *off* state), there is only leakage current from emitter to collector. In the saturated mode (or *on* state), there is maximum current from emitter to collector, limited only by external components. When the transistor is in the active mode, the current from emitter to collector is controlled, usually linearly, by the current from emitter to base.

The mode of operation used most in analog designs is the active mode. The cut off and saturated modes are used mostly in switching circuits (which are covered in detail in Chapter 8). All three modes will be discussed here, since each points out the importance of several transistor parameters.

The transistor is usually biased as follows: forward bias across the base-emitter junction and reverse bias across the base-collector junction. This is illustrated for both npn and pnp types in Fig. 2-6. The base-emitter and base-collector junctions may be considered as diodes that are either forward or reverse biased, as illustrated in Fig. 2-6B. Of more practical importance is the fact that the base terminal voltage is usually closer to the supply voltage (V_{CC}) than the emitter terminal voltage, and the collector terminal voltage is closer to the supply voltage than either the base or emitter. With the transistor biased in this manner, a small change in the amount of base current (I_B in Fig. 2-6A) will result in a larger change in the collector current (I_C). It is this phenomenon that allows voltage, current, and power gain in a circuit.

When a transistor is used in a circuit, there are several important parameters that must be taken into account. These

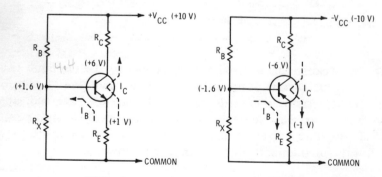

(A) Simple circuits showing proper bias potentials.

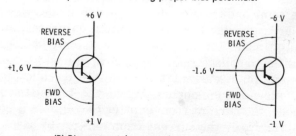

(B) Bias potentials across the pn junctions.

Fig. 2-6. Bias polarities for npn and pnp bipolar devices.

parameters are illustrated in the three circuits of Fig. 2-7 and are discussed in detail below. The twelve characteristics that should be taken into account when selecting a transistor for a circuit and in designing the circuit are:

1. $V_{(BR)CBO}$—This is the collector-to-base breakdown voltage (reverse bias condition) above which the device may be destroyed. The transistor selected for a particular circuit must have a $V_{(BR)CBO}$ (or just V_{CBO}) rating higher than the highest voltage expected to exist from collector to base in that circuit.

2. $V_{(BR)EBO}$—This is the emitter-to-base breakdown voltage (reverse bias direction) which, if exceeded, may cause the transistor to fail. The device selected for a circuit must have a $V_{(BR)EBO}$ (or just V_{EBO}) rating higher than the greatest voltage expected to appear across the base-emitter junction. In most analog circuits, the base-emitter voltage seldom exceeds about 1 V in either the forward or reverse direction, so if this parameter is not specified, the circuit will probably still function properly and safely.

3. $V_{(BR)CEV}$—This is the collector-to-emitter breakdown voltage with the device in the cutoff mode. If this voltage is exceeded, the transistor may be destroyed. This parameter must usually exceed the circuit power-supply voltage (or conversely, the supply voltage must be held below the value of this parameter) if the circuit is to operate safely. If $V_{(BR)CEV}$ or V_{CEV} is not specified, V_{CEO} can be used, since it is usually a lower value.

4. I_{CBO}—This parameter, the leakage current from collector to base when that junction is reverse biased, is of major importance when designing transistor circuits. This leakage current increases rapidly with increases in the temperature of the transistor junction. Furthermore, excess leakage current will affect the collector current from 10 to 1000 times its own value (see the definition of beta, or h_{fe}, below). This can cause the circuit operating point to shift far enough to make it operate improperly or even destroy itself. Thus, when choosing a transistor for a circuit, choose one that has a very low I_{CBO}. This will simplify stabilization of the stage and the

calculations required to bias the stage. While most present silicon transistors for small-signal applications have leakage currents low enough to be ignored in designing a circuit, this parameter must be checked if a circuit is to operate as it was designed.

5. I_{CEV}—This is the leakage current from collector to emitter with the base reverse biased. This parameter is usually specified only for power transistors, since for small-signal transistors its effect is nullified when I_{CBO} is minimized. I_{CEV} is approximately equal to $I_{CBO} \times$ beta.

6. $V_{CE(sat)}$—This is the voltage from collector to emitter when the transistor is saturated. (A further increase in base current causes no further increase in collector current.) It is also the minimum voltage that must be maintained from the collector to emitter of the device if it is to continue to exhibit transistor action. Its effect is to reduce the allowable signal swing available at the collector of the transistor. It is usually specified at a specific current ($I_{C(sat)}$) and is about 0.5 to 1.0 volt. While this parameter is most important in switching circuits, it does have an effect in analog circuits. This effect is described in Chapter 3.

7. $V_{BE(sat)}$—This is the base-to-emitter voltage when the transistor is saturated. It is sometimes specified as V_{BE} for a given current (rather than saturation) and sometimes is depicted graphically to show V_{BE} for a range of base currents. It is important in switching circuits and must be included in the bias calculations of most analog circuits.

8. $I_{C(max)}$—This parameter, the maximum collector current that the device can safely handle, is usually listed under "Absolute Maximum Ratings" on a transistor data sheet. Circuitry must be designed so that this value is never exceeded.

9. $I_{B(sat)}$—The base current at which the transistor is saturated and at which $V_{BE(sat)}$ is specified is called $I_{B(sat)}$. A further increase in I_B over $I_{B(sat)}$ will not result in an increase in collector current.

10. P_T—The total power that a transistor can safely dissipate, P_T, is approximately equal to $V_{CE} \times I_C$. The base-emitter junction also contributes to P_T but is usually so

small compared to $V_{CE} \times I_C$, that it can be ignored. When a circuit is designed and a transistor selected, it is important to assure that $V_{CE} \times I_C$ will be less than P_T at all possible points on the operating curve. If this is not done, the transistor may be damaged. P_T is usually specified at a temperature of 25°C (room temperature), and this temperature is normally valid as long as no power is applied to the circuit. In most applications it is wise to choose a transistor whose P_T is at least twice $V_{CE} \times I_C$. This will ensure that the device will operate properly at the operating junction and case temperatures.

11. β—Called beta or h_{fe}, this is the current gain of a transistor in the common-emitter configuration. (The circuits of Fig. 2-7 are all "common-emitter" circuits. The signal is applied across the base and emitter and removed

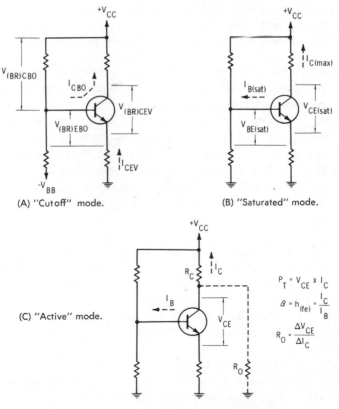

(A) "Cutoff" mode.

(B) "Saturated" mode.

(C) "Active" mode.

$$P_T = V_{CE} \times I_C$$

$$\beta = h_{(fe)} = \frac{I_C}{I_B}$$

$$R_O = \frac{\Delta V_{CE}}{\Delta I_C}$$

Fig. 2-7. Three modes of operation of the bipolar transistor.

across the collector and emitter. The emitter is the *common* terminal for input and output, hence the name for the circuit configuration.) Beta may be specified as a range of values (50-200), listed as a set of values at specific collector currents (10 @ 1 mA, 20 @ 10 mA, etc.), or presented on a graph of h_{fe} versus I_C. Regardless of how it is specified, it is one of the most important transistor parameters. Beta is defined as the ratio of collector current to base current in a device. If a device has a beta of 100, a 1-mA change in base current will result in a 100-mA change in collector current. This represents a "current gain," or amplification. There are two types of beta—dc and ac. The dc beta is defined as I_C/I_B. The ac beta is defined as $\Delta I_C/\Delta I_B$ (Δ being "the change in") and is covered more thoroughly in the chapters on analog amplifiers. The dc beta (or just beta, since ac beta will be specified wherever it is used) is a factor in the biasing of a stage, its stability, and its current, voltage, and/or power gain.

12. R_O—This is the last of the twelve transistor characteristics to be defined. It is the effective resistance from collector to emitter that is seen in parallel with the collector resistor (R_C in Fig. 2-7C) when looking at the output of a stage. It is important when matching one stage to another and when matching input to output impedances. It is defined as the change in V_{CE} divided by the change in I_C required to cause the change in V_{CE}, ($R_O = \Delta V_{CE}/\Delta I_C$). It usually must be calculated from the transistor characteristic curves.

The circuit of Fig. 2-8 should help to tie all of these parameters together. It shows a single-stage amplifier, biased in the active region, and a set of transistor parameters and characteristic curves. All of the parameters important in a circuit design are included. The value of I_{CBO} has been exaggerated considerably for the purpose of showing its effect on the circuit operation.

Since the supply voltage (V_{CC}) is 20 V, the $V_{(BR)CBO}$ and $V_{(BR)CEV}$ values are not exceeded, and since the base can never go negative, the $V_{(BR)EBO}$ rating of the transistor is not exceeded. No more than 18 mA can flow in the circuit even if the transistor is shorted, so a safe level is maintained within the $I_{C(max)}$ rating of the transistor. The power dissipation, as shown in Fig. 2-8, is $V_{CE} \times I_C = 8.88$ V $\times 0.0101$ A, or 89.6 mW, well below the 250-mW (0.25 W) P_T rating. The values of $V_{BE(sat)}$ and $I_{B(sat)}$ do not concern us in this circuit, while $V_{BE} = 0.77$ V

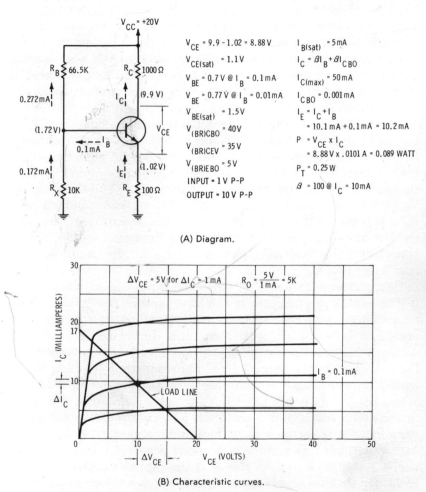

$V_{CE} = 9.9 - 1.02 = 8.88$ V
$V_{CE(sat)} = 1.1$ V
$V_{BE} = 0.7$ V @ $I_B = 0.1$ mA
$V_{BE} = 0.77$ V @ $I_B = 0.01$ mA
$V_{BE(sat)} = 1.5$ V
$V_{(BR)CBO} = 40$ V
$V_{(BR)CEV} = 35$ V
$V_{(BR)EBO} = 5$ V
INPUT = 1 V P-P
OUTPUT = 10 V P-P

$I_{B(sat)} = 5$ mA
$I_C = \beta I_B + \beta I_{CBO}$
$I_{C(max)} = 50$ mA
$I_{CBO} = 0.001$ mA
$I_E = I_C + I_B$
$\quad = 10.1$ mA $+ 0.1$ mA $= 10.2$ mA
$P = V_{CE} \times I_C$
$\quad = 8.88$ V x .0101 A $= 0.089$ WATT
$P_T = 0.25$ W
$\beta = 100$ @ $I_C = 10$ mA

(A) Diagram.

$\Delta V_{CE} = 5$ V for $\Delta I_C = 1$ mA $R_O = \dfrac{5\,V}{1\,mA} = 5$K

$I_B = 0.1$ mA

LOAD LINE

(B) Characteristic curves.

Fig. 2-8. A transistor circuit with a set of typical parameters and characteristic curves.

@ $I_B = 0.01$ mA is used in the calculation of R_B and R_X. The value of V_{CC} is used to determine one point on the load line (20 V V_{CE} at 0 mA I_C), and the characteristic curves are used to calculate R_O.

That leaves the currents in the circuit. The collector current (I_C) is made up of beta times the base current (I_B) plus beta times the leakage current (I_{CBO}). Note that this causes the collector voltage to be 0.1 volt less than the 10.0 volts which would be present if the transistor were "perfect"—without leakage currents and with an I_C exactly equal to beta times I_B. This is, of course, only a one-percent change, even with exaggerated leakage currents. Using good silicon transistors, many circuit designs can ignore the leakage currents. Nevertheless, the value of I_{CBO} should be checked to make sure that it is negligible. The equation for I_E and the value of the current through R_B are given in Fig. 2-8.

The load line for the circuit is plotted on the characteristic curves by using two points. The first, on the V_{CE} axis, is chosen to be equal to V_{CC}, the supply voltage. The second point requires calculation. It is on the I_C axis and is the maximum current that can flow when the transistor is saturated. The equation is $V_{CC} - V_{CE(sat)}$, which is the available voltage, divided by $R_C + R_E$, the total circuit resistance. The line drawn between the two points is the dc load line. The *quiescent*, or no-input, operating point is usually chosen to be near the center of the load line.

In the circuit of Fig. 2-8, when the input signal rises from 0 V to +0.5 V, an increase in the base current results. This increase in base current causes a corresponding, but larger, increase in collector current. Assuming that +0.5 V causes a 0.05-mA increase in the quiescent I_B, the collector current will increase 5 mA, for a total I_C of approximately 15 mA. This causes the voltage at the collector to drop from 9.9 V to 4.9 V. When the input swings to −0.5 V, it causes a 0.05-mA decrease in the quiescent I_B and therefore a 5-mA decrease in collector current. The collector voltage is now increased from 9.9 V to 14.9 V because less voltage is dropped across R_C. In this manner, a 1-volt peak-to-peak signal at the input (base) causes an identical (but inverted) 10-volt peak-to-peak signal at the collector. The stage in Fig. 2-8 has a current gain of 100, a voltage gain of 10, and a power gain of $10 \times 100 = 1000$ (30 dB).

Testing Bipolar Transistors

Just as an ohmmeter can be used to test a diode, it can be used to test most bipolar transistors. The method is shown pictorially in Fig. 2-9. Remember to use a high ohms scale (R × 1000 or R × 10K) to avoid damaging the device under test. Back-to-front ratios should be at least 1000 to 1. The reading from collector to emitter with the base open (this is really checking I_{CEO}) should be almost infinite in both directions. Simply reverse the meter leads from the polarities shown to check pnp transistors.

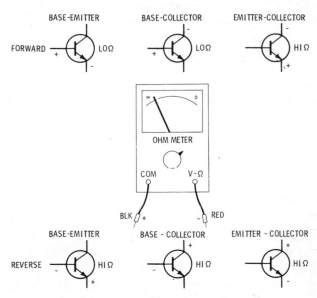

Fig. 2-9. Transistor testing with the ohmmeter.

FIELD-EFFECT TRANSISTORS

There are two categories of field-effect transistors. These are the junction field-effect transistor (JFET or simply FET) and the insulated-gate field-effect transistor (IGFET or MOSFET; MOSFET stands for metal-oxide-semiconductor FET).

Like bipolar transistors, these transistors come in two types —n-types and p-types. As with bipolar transistors, the n and the p determine the polarity of the voltages that are applied to the transistors.

Field-effect transistors operate in one or two of three modes —the depletion mode (JFET), the enhancement mode (type C IGFET), and the enhancement-depletion mode (normal

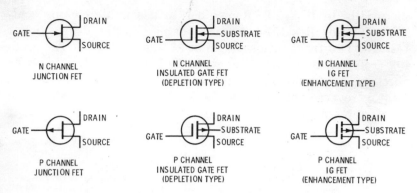

Fig. 2-10. Schematic symbols for field-effect transistors.

IGFET). Figure 2-10 shows the schematic symbols for several types of FET's. The broken-line symbol for the enhancement type IGFET symbolizes the "normally off" characteristic of the device. In IGFET applications, the substrate terminal is usually connected to ground or to the source terminal.

FET Characteristics

The major difference between a junction FET and an insulated-gate FET is the input impedance. The input impedance of an IGFET is approximately 10 megohms, while the input impedance of a junction FET is about 1 megohm.

The field-effect transistor operates in basically the same manner as the vacuum tube. The source-to-drain current is controlled by the voltage applied to the gate. With a junction FET, the gate is always reverse biased with respect to the source terminal, while an insulated-gate FET may be biased either forward or reverse (or not biased at all).

From a practical standpoint, the JFET and type-B IGFET are most worthy of discussion. The enhancement (type-C) IGFET operates in a similar fashion, except that it must be forward biased in order for source-drain current to flow. The usual bias configuration and a typical set of characteristic curves for an n-type JFET are shown in Fig. 2-11. Note that the bias configuration for a JFET is very similar to that used with a vacuum tube. Resistor R_S is used to develop enough voltage to provide reverse bias on the gate.

In the area of the curve bounded by I_{DSS} (the zero-bias drain current) and V_P (the "pinch-off" voltage), the JFET acts very

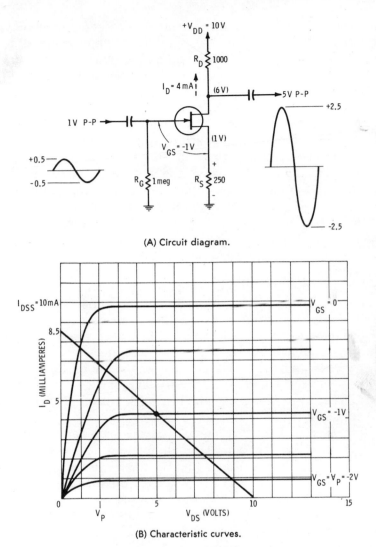

(A) Circuit diagram.

(B) Characteristic curves.

Fig. 2-11. JFET biasing and typical characteristic curves.

much like a resistor whose value may be controlled by varying V_{GS} (the voltage from gate to source). This makes the JFET useful for many control applications, since the resistance will vary from a low of $R_{DS(on)}$ (drain to source resistance with zero bias) to a very high value when V_{GS} approaches V_P. The area of the curve to the right of V_P is the region where the JFET is used for signal amplification. A load line is drawn from the maximum I_D point (found the same way as I_C for bipolar transistors) to the maximum V_{DS} point (the supply voltage) ; the quiescent operating point is found on the characteristic curves, and the resistor values are chosen for operation at this point.

When a change in the voltage from gate to source is caused by an input voltage change (refer again to Fig. 2-11), a change in drain current is caused. If a +0.5-volt change in V_{GS} causes a 2.5-mA increase in I_D, the drain voltage will swing down to 3.5 V. When the input swings to −0.5 V, the drain current decreases, causing an increase in the voltage at the drain terminal. A 1-volt peak-to-peak input signal has been amplified to 5 volts peak-to-peak. The current gain in this circuit is I_D divided by I_G. Since I_G is extremely small, large current gains (and therefore power gains) can be achieved using the FET. Its high input impedance makes it ideal for many audio and rf applications.

The basic circuit configuration and a set of the characteristic curves for a type-B (depletion-enhancement) n-channel IGFET are illustrated in Fig. 2-12. As mentioned earlier, the IGFET has a much higher input impedance than the JFET. The input impedance of the IGFET connected as shown in Fig. 2-12 is approximately equal to the value of R_G, which is usually between 1 and 10 megohms. This makes it very useful in rf circuits or sensitive control circuits, since it does not tend to load down the source.

Referring to Fig. 2-12, note that the gate terminal of an IGFET need not be biased at all for the device to operate properly. This makes interfacing the device to its input source extremely simple. As was the case with the JFET, in the area of the curve to the left of V_P the transistor acts like a resistor from source to drain whose value is variable by changing V_{GS}. Circuit operation in Fig. 2-12 is identical to the operation of the JFET circuit in Fig. 2-11.

Some of the important parameters that must be considered when designing with field-effect transistors (junction or insulated gate) are:

1. V_{DS}—The maximum voltage that should be applied across the drain and source terminals.
2. V_{GS}—The maximum dc voltage that can be applied between gate and source without damaging the device.

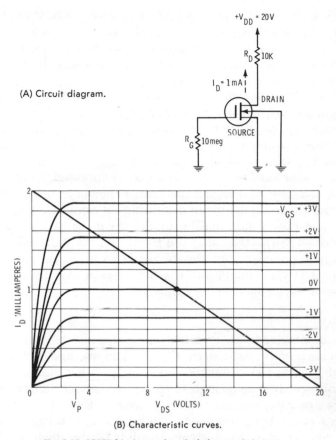

(A) Circuit diagram.

(B) Characteristic curves.

Fig. 2-12. IGFET biasing and typical characteristic curves.

3. V_{GS}—The peak voltage that can be applied between gate and source of an IGFET (usually specified as $\pm$ V).

4. $I_{D(max)}$—The maximum drain current allowable through the device. This parameter may be specified as a function of the power dissipation of the device, rather than as an absolute value. (This is similar to rating a resistor in terms of power, rather than voltage or current. In the FET, the maximum voltage is also specified.)

5. I_{DSS}—The drain-to-source current with zero volts between the gate and source (zero bias). This parameter is needed to locate the operating point of the circuit. If it is not specified, it can usually be extrapolated from the characteristic curves for the device.

6. $R_{DS(on)}$—The drain-to-source resistance when the device is on (zero gate bias) and operated in the ohmic area to the left of the pinch-off region. When the transistor is used as a variable resistor in this region, $R_{DS(on)}$ is an important parameter.

7. V_P—The pinch-off voltage defines the area in which the transistor will operate linearly as an amplifier. If V_{GS} exceeds the pinch-off voltage, the device operates in the same manner as a cut-off transistor—a further increase in V_{GS} will result in no change in I_D.

8. y_{fs}—Forward transconductance (expressed in mhos) is a measure of the voltage gain achievable using the device. It is important in designing an amplifier stage.

9. G_{PS}—Power gain in dB provides the information that cannot be calculated using the $P = E \times I$ formula. (Since the input impedance of the device is so high, the input current is very small, and the power-gain calculation would show G_{PS} approaching infinity).

Testing and Handling FET's

The ohmmeter method of testing diodes and bipolar transistors must *not* be used with FET's. The voltage and current available from the ohmmeter (no matter what range it is set on) will probably be enough to cause permanent damage to the junction or gate, making the FET useless. Furthermore, static charges (like those created by walking across a rug on a dry day) are enough to destroy insulated-gate devices. These should never be handled unless all terminals are connected (shorted externally). Most IGFET's are packaged with shorting rings which should only be removed *after* the device has been installed in the proper circuit.

SCR AND TRIAC THYRISTORS

The silicon controlled rectifier (SCR) and the triac are both members of the family of semiconductors called thyristors. The SCR is called a reverse blocking thyristor, while the triac is called a bidirectional thyristor. The difference between an SCR and a triac is that an SCR may be turned on only when its anode is positive with respect to its cathode; a triac may be turned on with either terminal (designated MT1 and MT2 for

ANODE (A)

GATE (G)

CATHODE (K)

(A) Silicon controlled rectifier (SCR).

MAIN TERMINAL 2 (MT2)

GATE (G)

MAIN TERMINAL 1 (MT1)

(B) Triac.

Fig. 2-13. Schematic symbols.

Main Terminal 1 and Main Terminal 2, respectively) positive with respect to the other. In essence, a triac is two SCR's connected in opposite directions but using a single gate terminal. The schematic symbols of the SCR and triac are shown in Fig. 2-13.

The SCR and triac are "bistable" semiconductor devices. This means that they have two discrete states and will remain in any one state until acted upon by some external stimulus. The two states are off and on.

SCR Operation

Fig. 2-14A shows an SCR connected in a control circuit. (The voltages and currents shown in Fig. 2-14 are defined in a following section entitled "Thyristor Characteristics.") The SCR is shown in the off, or nonconducting state. In respect to the circuit components, the SCR functions like a reverse-biased diode, even though the polarity from anode to cathode is that required for forward bias. The SCR will remain in the off state until the gate terminal is made positive with respect to the cathode by closing switch S1. When S1 is closed (Fig. 2-14B), the SCR will switch to the on state, conducting current through the load resistor (R_L) and having a voltage drop of between 0.5 and 1.5 volts (very similar to a conducting diode). When the SCR is conducting, the gate voltage may be removed without causing the SCR to turn off (Fig. 2-14C). To turn the SCR off, the current through it must be reduced to a value below its "holding current" (explained in the section titled Thyristor Characteristics later in this chapter). This is accomplished by opening switch S2 (Fig. 2-14D), which reduces the SCR current to zero. If switch S2 is returned to the closed position, the SCR will remain off until the gate is again "triggered." An alternative method of turning off the SCR is shown by dash lines in Fig. 2-14C. The switch connected across the SCR may be momentarily closed, applying zero volts from anode to cathode of the SCR, thus reducing the current through the SCR to zero.

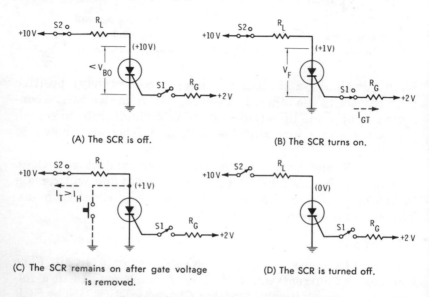

(A) The SCR is off.

(B) The SCR turns on.

(C) The SCR remains on after gate voltage is removed.

(D) The SCR is turned off.

Fig. 2-14. Operation of SCR in simple circuit.

The SCR is a versatile control device. It can be used to replace relays in many instances and can be used to indicate the presence of transient phenomena (once-in-a-while happenings), since the SCR will remain in the on state even if the gate signal is removed.

Triac Operation

The triac operates in exactly the same manner as the SCR, except that the voltage from main terminal 1 to main terminal 2 may be either positive or negative. Although the triac will operate in four modes, only two are of real interest in practical circuitry. These modes are illustrated in Fig. 2-15.

Since the triac, connected as in Fig. 2-15, acts exactly as an SCR, regardless of the voltage from MT1 to MT2, it makes an excellent "ac SCR." As long as the gate remains positive with respect to MT1, the triac will conduct both halves of an ac current. Using ac current or voltage across the triac has another advantage. The load circuit does not have to be disconnected to turn the triac off. If the gate voltage is removed, the triac will turn off as the ac signal swings through zero. (When there is zero volts across the triac, there is no current through it, and it will turn off.)

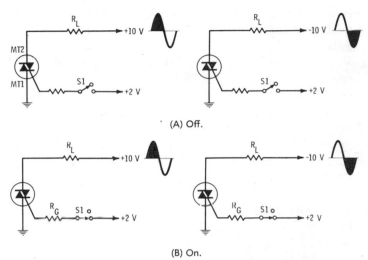

(A) Off.

(B) On.

Fig. 2-15. Operation of the triac.

The triac is used most often as a relay replacement in ac circuits. It also has other uses in control and regulator circuits, since a small dc voltage on the gate can control a large ac load through MT1 and MT2.

Thyristor Characteristics

The characteristics for the SCR are the same, in most cases, as the characteristics for the triac because they are similar devices. Where differences exist in the descriptions below, they will be pointed out. The important thyristor characteristics that should be considered when selecting an SCR or triac or designing a circuit around either device are:

1. I_T—Specified either as an rms or an average current, this is the maximum continuous current that may flow through the thyristor without causing permanent harm. Choose a device whose I_T is greater than the maximum current expected in the circuit.

2. V_{RM}—This is the peak reverse blocking voltage for an SCR and is analogous to the V_{BR}, PIV, or PRV of a rectifier diode. Its value must not be exceeded.

3. V_{BO}—This is the forward breakover voltage for either an SCR or a triac. If the forward voltage across the thyristor is allowed to exceed this value, the device may turn on without a command (or input) signal being applied to the gate.

4. V_{GT}—This is the dc gate trigger voltage and is usually specified as a range from minimum to maximum. The minimum V_{GT} is the value above which the device *may* turn on. The maximum V_{GT} is the value above which the device *will always* turn on. Circuit design must keep the gate voltage below $V_{GT(min)}$ when the thyristor is to be off and should cause the gate voltage to approach $V_{GT(max)}$ to insure proper turn-on of the device. Usually the $V_{GT(typical)}$ value is sufficient at normal temperatures.

5. V_{GM}—This is the maximum gate voltage that can be applied without causing damage to the device. Care should be taken to insure that it is not exceeded.

6. I_H—The holding current is the current below which a conducting thyristor, in the absence of a gate signal, will switch to the off state. In circuit design, the current through the device must exceed I_H when the device is required to be turned on.

7. I_{GT}—The gate trigger current is usually specified as minimum, nominal (or typical), and maximum. It is the current required by the gate to turn on the device reliably. The circuit design should provide for enough gate current (at V_{GT}) to turn the device on reliably.

8. I_{GM}—The maximum gate-current value, I_{GM}, should never be exceeded. The gate current should be limited by external circuit components.

Two other characteristics, the critical dv/dt (rate of rise of off-state voltage) and di/dt (rate of rise of on-state current), are important if the thyristor is to be used in a high-frequency circuit, where heavy surge currents (di/dt) might be drawn. These ratings, expressed as volts per microsecond and amperes per microsecond, respectively, should exceed the rates of rise to be expected in the circuit which uses the thyristor.

UNIJUNCTION AND PROGRAMMABLE
UNIJUNCTION TRANSISTORS

The unijunction transistor (UJT) and programmable unijunction transistor (PUT) are three-terminal semiconductors that act quite differently from bipolar or field-effect transistors. They are used primarily in signal-source and thyristor-control circuits but are also useful in signal-detection and time-delay applications.

The Unijunction Transistor (UJT)

The schematic symbol for the UJT is shown in Fig. 2-16A, and the most common circuit configuration is depicted in Fig. 2-16B. It is a simple relaxation oscillator whose frequency is determined by R_E and C_E. The UJT acts like a resistor with 5000 to 10,000 ohms resistance from base 1 to base 2 as long as the emitter-to-base 1 junction is reverse biased. This is called the interbase resistance. When the emitter-to-base 1 junction is forward biased by a voltage (V_P in Fig. 2-16B), the interbase resistance drops to a low value. This allows a current, limited by R_{B1} and R_{B2} (Fig. 2-16B), to flow from base 1 to base 2. Once the emitter-to-base 1 junction is forward biased, the voltage at the emitter will decrease, due to increased cur-

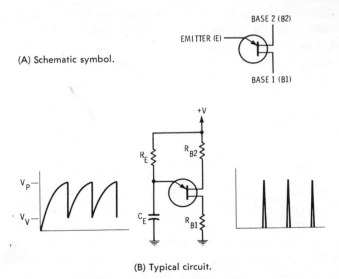

(A) Schematic symbol.

(B) Typical circuit.

Fig. 2-16. The unijunction transistor.

rent, until the voltage is no longer high enough to keep the junction forward biased (approximately $V_{E(sat)}$). When this happens, the interbase resistance rises rapidly to its initial value, the emitter-base junction ceases to conduct, and the emitter voltage must be raised back up to V_P to start the cycle again.

Of particular importance is the value of V_P at which the emitter-to-base 1 junction is forward biased. This voltage is related to the voltage from base 1 to base 2 by a factor η, called the *intrinsic standoff ratio* of the device. The equation is:

$$V_P = \eta\, V_{bb} + V_D$$

where,

V_P is the peak-point voltage,
V_{bb} is the voltage from base 1 to base 2,
V_D is the voltage across the emitter diode portion of the emitter-to-base 1 junction (usually 0.4 to 0.7 volt),
η is a constant whose value usually ranges from about 0.45 to 0.85.

The value of V_P must be known in order to calculate effectively the values of frequency-determining components for a relaxation oscillator or timer. The value of V_P is also needed to determine where the device will switch on when it is used as a sensing device.

Fig. 2-17 is the same circuit as Fig. 2-16B with each of the important UJT parameters identified. Resistor R_{B2} in the circuit serves three purposes: it limits the device current, it stabilizes the value of η, and it simplifies the equation for V_P. Note that the voltage at B1 is also related to η. The parameters

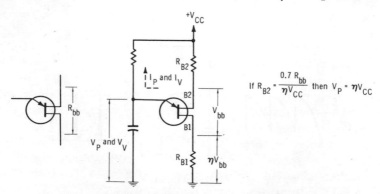

Fig. 2-17. A typical UJT circuit with the important parameters shown.

that should be considered when designing with a unijunction transistor are:

1. I_P—This "peak-point" current is the minimum current that must be supplied to the emitter, at voltage V_P, for the UJT to turn on reliably.
2. I_V—This "valley" current is the minimum value to which the emitter current must be reduced, at voltage V_V, for the UJT to return to the high-resistance (off) state.
3. V_P—The "peak-point" voltage is the emitter voltage above which the emitter-to-base 1 junction conducts. It is approximately equal to $\eta\ V_{bb}$.
4. V_V—The "valley" voltage is the voltage that will exist between the emitter and base 1 of the UJT when it is in the on state. The emitter-to-base 1 voltage must be reduced to a value below this potential if the UJT is to return to the off state.
5. R_{bb}—The "interbase resistance" is the resistance from base 1 to base 2 with no emitter current. Its value must be known to define the circuit elements properly.
6. η—The "intrinsic standoff ratio" is the ratio of V_P to V_{bb} in the unijunction circuit.

There are also maximum forward and reverse voltage ratings and an absolute maximum power rating that should be taken into account when the circuit is designed and the UJT selected. These types of ratings have been discussed previously for diodes, bipolar transistors, and field-effect transistors; they are much the same for the UJT.

The Programmable Unijunction Transistor (PUT)

The programmable unijunction transistor (PUT) has several advantages over the normal UJT. Among them are the ability to "program" the peak-point voltage, V_P, and the intrinsic standoff ratio, η, using external components. This permits the user to tailor the PUT characteristics to fit his particular requirements.

The schematic symbol for a PUT is illustrated in Fig. 2-18. As Fig. 2-18 shows, the anode, cathode, and gate of the PUT are analogous to the emitter, base 1, and base 2, respectively, of the UJT. The usual circuit configuration for a PUT, equivalent to the UJT relaxation oscillator, is shown in Fig. 2-19.

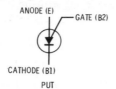

Fig. 2-18. UJT and PUT symbols showing terminal equivalence.

The input voltage, from V_{CC} through R_A and applied to the anode, causes the PUT to function from cathode to gate in a manner identical to that of a normal unijunction transistor. The real differences lie in the control the designer has over the critical device parameters.

The actual "programming" of the PUT is done through the proper selection of R1 and R2 in Fig. 2-19. The voltage at the gate (V_G) determines the peak-point voltage (V_P) required at the anode to turn on the PUT. In the configuration shown:

$$V_P = V_G + V_D$$

where,

V_P is the peak-point voltage,

V_G is the gate voltage,

V_D is the voltage across the anode diode portion of the anode-to-cathode junction.

Since V_G can be set independently of V_{CC}, the intrinsic stand-off ratio is effectively varied by variations of R1 and R2. The equivalent source impedance at the gate terminal (the parallel combination of R1 and R2) determines the I_P and I_V of the PUT so that the device can be tailored to operate over a wide selection of currents in the anode circuit (R_A). The Thevinin equivalent voltage (V_T) of the R1-R2 network shown in Fig. 2-19 is equal to V_G.

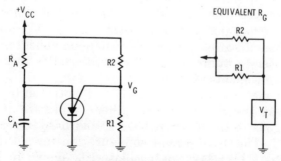

Fig. 2-19. The PUT relaxation oscillator.

The parameters listed for the PUT are similar to those listed for the UJT, except that I_P and I_V are usually specified for three or more values of equivalent R_G to provide the information necessary to program the device in the desired operating area. As with all other semiconductor devices, the "absolute maximum ratings" should never be exceeded, or irreversible damage to the device may result.

MISCELLANEOUS SEMICONDUCTOR DEVICES

This category of semiconductors is very broad indeed. There are a great many special-purpose devices that have been created to fill specific circuit and application needs.

The "high spots" of some of the more interesting and more important of these devices will be covered in the following paragraphs. Since most of these devices are mutations of existing devices, the detailed descriptions of their parameters are not provided, with the exception of the zener diode, which is covered in detail.

The Zener Diode

The zener, or reverse-breakdown, diode is a two-terminal device whose voltage (at operating point) remains essentially constant regardless of the current through it. In this sense, it is much like the older gas-filled regulator tube, and it is used primarily as a reference voltage source in power-supply or signal-sensing circuitry.

The schematic symbol for the zener diode, its characteristic curve, and the usual circuit configuration are shown in Fig. 2-20. As can be seen from the graph in Fig. 2-20B, when the zener is reverse biased, there is very little current through it until the zener voltage, V_Z, is reached. When this happens, current through the diode increases rapidly, limited primarily by external components, and the voltage across the diode remains constant at V_Z.

The important zener characteristics are:

1. V_Z—The nominal zener voltage (V_Z) of the diode is usually specified at a specific I_Z (zener current). This voltage will remain relatively constant from a low value of current (the knee current, I_{ZK}, in Fig. 2-20B) to the maxi-

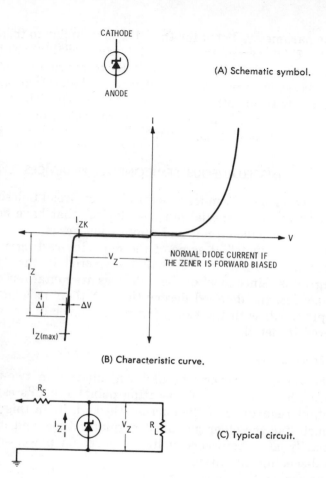

CATHODE

ANODE

(A) Schematic symbol.

I_{ZK}

V_Z

NORMAL DIODE CURRENT IF
THE ZENER IS FORWARD BIASED

I_Z

ΔI

ΔV

$I_{Z(max)}$

(B) Characteristic curve.

R_S

I_Z

V_Z

R_L

(C) Typical circuit.

Fig. 2-20. The zener diode.

mum current rating of the diode (which can be obtained from the device power rating).

2. I_Z—The zener current at which V_Z is specified is the value of current which would normally be sent through the device in a circuit for optimum performance. It is not necessary, however, to maintain I_Z at the specified value. As long as I_Z is between I_{ZK} and $I_{Z(max)}$, the device will work.

3. Z_Z—The zener impedance, Z_Z, is equal to the change in V_Z divided by the change in I_Z needed to cause V_Z to change.

$$Z_Z = \frac{\Delta V_Z}{\Delta I_Z}$$

This impedance is important whenever the diode is used as a coupling device (where Z_Z equals the equivalent series resistance to signal changes) and is usually specified at I_Z. The zener impedance is also a measure of how well the diode will perform under changing current conditions (such as ripple on the supply voltage).

4. P_T—The total power dissipation of the device must be known if the maximum allowable zener current is to be found. The P_T rating should never be exceeded if the device is not to be damaged. To find the maximum allowable zener current, divide P_T by V_Z. ($I = P/E$). The zener current should not be allowed to exceed this value.

In actual use, the value of R_S (Fig. 2-20C) is chosen so that enough current flows through the diode to maintain its zener voltage, and enough current flows through R_L at the zener voltage. Since R_L is usually circuitry whose effective impedance changes as the circuit turns on or off (or whatever else it does), R_S must be chosen so that the zener current will be at least I_{ZK} when the load is heavy (R_L small) and less than $I_{Z(max)}$ when the load is light (R_L large). When this is properly done, changes in R_L, although they cause changes in I_Z, do not affect the total current through R_S, and the voltage supplied to R_L is therefore maintained at V_Z.

The Light-Sensitive Transistor

The light-sensitive transistor is a device whose collector current is controlled by the amount of light falling on it. Its symbol is shown in Fig. 2-21. The base lead is not present in all "photo transistors," but if the base terminal is brought out, the quiescent operating conditions of the transistor can be set. These transistors are used to convert variations in light intensity to electrical signals.

The Four-Layer Diode

The four-layer diode symbol is shown in Fig. 2-22. The device has two stable states—*on* and *off*. In the off state, it acts like a high resistance (usually more than 1 megohm). In the on state, it acts like a low resistance (usually less than 100 ohms). The four-layer diode will turn on when the voltage across it is raised above its V_{BR} (breakover voltage). The cur-

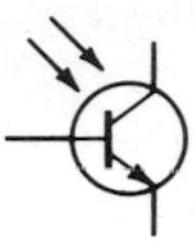

Fig. 2-21. Schematic symbol for
light-sensitive transistor.

Fig. 2-22. Schematic symbol for
four-layer diode.

rent through the diode increases rapidly (since its resistance decreases in the on state). To turn the four-layer diode off, the current through it must be reduced below I_H (the holding current). The four-layer diode acts like a normal silicon diode in the reverse-bias direction. Its reverse breakdown voltage should not be exceeded.

The Varactor Diode

The symbol for this device is shown in Fig. 2-23. In the forward-bias direction, it acts like a conventional diode. It is made, however, for operation in the reverse-bias mode. In this mode, the varactor appears to be a capacitor whose value is varied by changing the voltage across it. It is, in effect, a non-mechanical, electrically driven variable capacitor and can be very valuable for use in solid-state tuning circuits or in voltage-controlled rf oscillators. Capacitance values range from 5-10 pF to as much as 20-40 pF at voltages of from 3 to 10 volts.

The Field-Effect Diode

The field-effect diode, sometimes called a "current zener," is a device much like a field-effect transistor. It is designed so that a constant current, I_P, flows through it over a wide range of reverse bias voltages. The schematic symbol for the field-effect diode is shown in Fig. 2-24.

The diode conducts current I_P over the range of voltages from the knee voltage, V_K, up to the breakdown voltage. The characteristic curve closely resembles that of a zener diode with

Fig. 2-23. Schematic symbol for voltage-
variable capacitor diode.

Fig. 2-24. Schematic symbol for
field-effect diode.

the current and voltage axes interchanged. Diode current ratings range from about 0.2 mA to 5 mA. The constant-current characteristic of this device is useful in amplifier and power-supply design and in the generation of linear sawtooth waveforms.

The Light-Activated SCR

The light-activated SCR (LASCR) is an SCR whose conduction is controlled by the presence or absence of light applied to it, rather than by a signal on its gate lead (as in a conventional SCR).

Fig. 2-25. Schematic symbol for light-activated SCR.

SUMMARY

By this time, you should be familiar with the important parameters and characteristics of most of the solid-state devices in use today. In the following chapters, it will be assumed that the reader is familiar with the material in this chapter and with basic electronics theory (Ohm's law, Thevenin's theorem, etc.).

In the succeeding chapters, if a question arises as to why something was done in a particular way, the answer will probably be found by reviewing the material just presented. Solid-state circuit components will be used as building blocks, and their characteristics will be discussed further only if it is pertinent to the material being presented.

CHAPTER 3

Single-Stage Analog Amplifiers

The single-stage amplifier, whether it is implemented with bipolar or field-effect transistors, is the basic solid-state building block. It is used singly and in combinations to perform a great many functions—active filters, multivibrators, and oscillators to name a few.

The function of any amplifier is to increase one or more of the input-signal parameters—the voltage, the current, or the power. There are several configurations for using transistors, and each has its particular advantages and disadvantages. Some are characterized by voltage gain only, current gain only, or both voltage and current gain. Gain is defined as the ratio of output to input—current gain $A_i = I_O/I_I$, voltage gain $A_V = E_O/E_I$. Some configurations have high input impedances, some have low input impedances, and others have moderate input impedances. The configurations are also characterized by their high, low, or moderate output impedances.

The possible circuit configurations, their names, and their important characteristics are listed in Table 3-1. Two of the six circuit configurations shown in Table 3-1 are more widely used than the others: the common-emitter circuit for bipolar transistors and the common-source circuit for field-effect devices. This is because these circuits exhibit voltage, current,

Table 3-1. Transistor Circuit Configurations

Circuit	Configuration	Characteristics
Common Emitter		Voltage gain, current gain, low input impedance, moderate output impedance, output 180° out of phase with input
Common Base		Good voltage gain, no current gain, low input impedance, moderate output impedance, output in phase with input
Common Collector (emitter follower)		Good current gain, no voltage gain, high input impedance, low output Impedance, output in phase with input
Common Source		Good voltage gain, good current gain, high input impedance, moderate output impedance, output 180° out of phase with input
Common Gate		Voltage gain, no current gain, low input impedance, moderate output impedance, output in phase with input
Common Drain (source follower)		No voltage gain, good current gain, very high input impedance, low output impedance, output in phase with input

and power gain; while the others have only two of these gains at any time. These circuits get their names from the terminal that is "common" to both the input and the output signals.

One of the most important things that must be determined when designing an amplifier stage is the gain it will have. There are two types of gain in a transistor stage—dc gain and ac (or signal) gain. The dc gain is determined by the beta of the transistor or the transconductance of the FET being used in the circuit and is important for biasing the stage. The ac gain is more complex, since it is a function not only of the dc gain of the transistor, but also of some of the external circuit components.

THE COMMON-EMITTER CIRCUIT

The common-emitter circuit is the most often used bipolar-transistor circuit. The schematic for this circuit configuration is shown in Fig. 3-1. The base-emitter junction is forward-biased (the base positive with respect to the emitter for an npn transistor), and the base-collector junction is reverse-biased. These are the necessary conditions for transistor action. The collector current, I_C, is beta times the base current, or 100×0.05 mA = 5 mA, so that 5 volts is dropped across R_C. When the base current is increased through the introduction of an input voltage, as shown in Fig. 3-2A, the collector current is increased by a factor of 100 (the beta of the transistor), causing the voltage at the collector to decrease. When the base current is decreased as the input voltage goes below the +0.6-V level (Fig. 3-2B), the collector current decreases and the voltage drop across R_C decreases (the collector voltage increases).

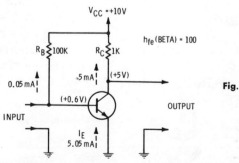

Fig. 3-1. A typical common-emitter circuit.

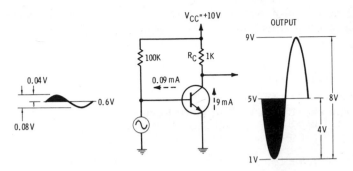

(A) Positive-going input signal, decreasing output signal.

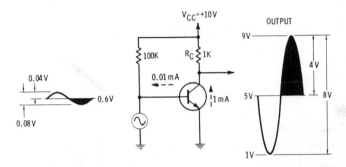

(B) Negative-going input signal, increasing output signal.

Fig. 3-2. Effect of applied input signal on stage output.

The result is a duplicate of the input waveform at the collector but 100 times as large and 180° out of phase.

The transistor shown in Fig. 3-2, however, must be a "perfect" transistor in order for it to behave exactly as just described. In actual practice, there are a number of limiting factors, so it is not possible to achieve a voltage gain of beta. This value may be approached but never reached. Fig. 3-3 shows one of these factors, the internal emitter resistance (r_e) of the transistor. This resistance, although small, introduces enough degenerative feedback into the circuit to bring the voltage gain of the stage down below beta. The value of r_e can be approximated from the formula:

$$r_e = \frac{26}{I_E}$$

where,

I_E is the dc emitter current in milliamperes.

The actual voltage gain of the stage can be calculated from the voltage gain equation for the common-emitter circuit of Fig. 3-3:

$$A_V = \frac{R_C}{r_e}$$

where,

A_V is the voltage gain of the stage,
R_C is the collector resistance in ohms,
r_e is the internal emitter resistance in ohms.

There is another transistor resistance that tends to bring the voltage gain of a stage below the value of beta. It is r_b, shown in Fig. 3-4. The value of r_b is usually between 200 and 1000 ohms for silicon transistors. This resistance, however, may normally be ignored without much, if any, effect on the circuit.

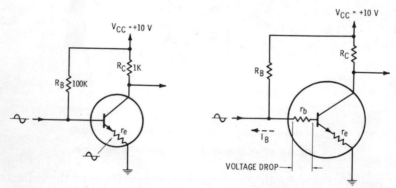

Fig. 3-3. Resistance r_e in a transistor.   Fig. 3-4. Resistance r_b in a transistor.

The simple circuit of Fig. 3-2 has another disadvantage; the voltage swing at the base is severely limited in the positive and negative directions by saturation and cutoff, respectively. If the base voltage is increased beyond about +0.7 volt, enough base current will flow to saturate the transistor, and further increases in base voltage (and therefore base current) will not result in any change in the collector current. If the base voltage is reduced below about 0.5 volt, there will not be enough potential to forward bias the base-emitter junction, and the transistor will not pass collector current.

The effects of r_e and the problem of the limited voltage swing at the base can be minimized through the addition of an external resistor, R_E, to the circuit, as shown in Fig. 3-5. From a practical standpoint, for all but very small values of R_E, any error introduced by neglecting r_e is insignificant when R_E is used.

We now have a practical amplifier circuit. However, several things remain to be done:

1. The voltage gain of the stage must be specified.
2. The magnitude of the output voltage swing must be specified.
3. The power-supply voltage must be specified to allow the required signal swing.
4. The transistor itself must be selected and biased so that it will operate properly.

Let us suppose that we wish to design a stage that has a voltage gain of 10, and we want a 10-volt peak-to-peak signal at the collector. The voltage gain for the circuit of Figs. 3-5 and 3-6 is:

$$A_V = \frac{R_C}{R_E} \qquad \text{(Eq. 3-1)}$$

where,
   A_V is the voltage gain,
   R_C is the collector resistance in ohms,
   R_E is the emitter resistance in ohms.

Since we wish to have $A_V = 10$, R_C will be 10 times the value of R_E. This means that for a 10-volt peak-to-peak swing at the collector, there will be a 1-volt peak-to-peak swing at the emitter for a total of eleven volts. Since a transistor normally re-

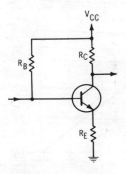

Fig. 3-5. Common-emitter stage with R_E added.

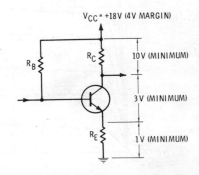

Fig. 3-6. Selecting V_{CC} for a transistor amplifier stage.

55

quires at least 2 or 3 volts across the collector-emitter terminals (use three times $V_{CE(sat)}$ for this value), the supply must be at least $11 + 3$, or 14, volts. Adding a safety margin of 25% produces $14 + 3.5$, or approximately 18, volts as the required supply voltage. For most circuits, the supply voltage will be at least 150 percent of the sum of the peak-to-peak voltages across R_C and R_E.

We know the ratio of R_C to R_E from the voltage-gain requirement, but how do we choose R_C and R_E? The answer to this lies in the characteristic curves for the transistor. From them, the total resistance in the circuit can be chosen. The individual values then involve only simple math to solve the ratio equation.

Refer to Fig. 3-7. Mark the power-supply voltage on the V_{CE} axis. This is the maximum value of voltage that can ever be across the transistor terminals. Next, mark on the I_C axis the maximum value of collector current that will be allowed in the circuit. A good rule of thumb for choosing this value is to make the maximum I_C equal to the maximum power dissipation divided by the supply voltage. In equation form, make

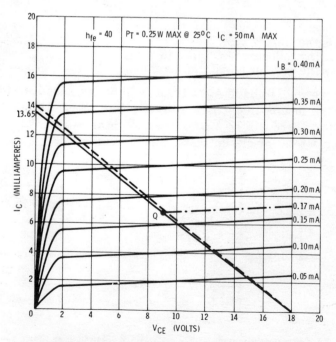

Fig. 3-7. Tentative and actual load lines drawn on characteristic curves.

$$I_{C(max)} = \frac{P_T}{V_{CC}} \qquad \text{(Eq. 3-2)}$$

If $I_{C(max)}$ is chosen this way, the transistor will not be required to dissipate more than one half of its maximum power rating at any time. In the case of the amplifier circuit being discussed, $I_{C(max)}$ will be 0.25 W/18 V = 0.014 A = 14 mA. The two points found thus far are at the ends of the dash line in Fig. 3-7.

In this case, $R_C + R_E$ = 18 V/14 mA = 1284 ohms. Next, the ratio of R_C to R_E is used to find the individual values. Let R_E be the unknown value. Since:

$$A_V = \frac{R_C}{R_E}$$

$$A_V = \frac{(R_C + R_E) - R_E}{R_E} \qquad \text{(Eq. 3-3)}$$

then,

$$R_E A_V = (R_C + R_E) - R_E$$
$$(R_E A_V) + R_E = R_C + R_E$$
$$R_E (A_V + 1) = R_C + R_E$$
$$R_E = \frac{R_C + R_E}{A_V + 1} \qquad \text{(Eq. 3-4)}$$

For the present example, R_E = 1284 ohms/11 = 117 ohms. Choose the closest standard resistor value of 120 ohms for R_E. Make R_C = 120 × 10 = 1200 ohms, also a standard value. The actual value of $R_C + R_E$ is now known to be 1200 + 120 = 1320 ohms. This value is substituted into the equation

$$I_{C(max)} = \frac{V_{CC}}{R_C + R_E} \qquad \text{(Eq. 3-5)}$$

to find the actual $I_{C(max)}$, which is 18 V/1320 ohms ≈ 13.65 mA. A new load line (solid line in Fig. 3-7) is now drawn from 18 V on the V_{CE} axis to 13.65 mA on the I_C axis. This is the actual load line for the circuit. It is now necessary to find the quiescent operating point (Q on the load line). Point Q is chosen so that the collector current will move equally in each direction along the load line. The proper collector current at the quiescent operating point is:

$$I_{C(Q)} = \frac{I_{C(max)}}{2} \qquad \text{(Eq. 3-6)}$$

In this case:

$$I_{C(Q)} = \frac{13.65}{2} = 6.8 \text{ mA}$$

The circuit now looks like the one shown in Fig. 3-8. All that remains to be done is to choose the value of R_B that will bias the transistor at the operating point. The amount of base current required is $I_{C(Q)}/\beta$, or 6.8 mA/40 = 0.17 mA. This current is supplied through R_B from V_{CC}. There are two ways to calculate R_B. One method is to make

$$R_B = \frac{(V_{CC} - V_{BE} - V_{RE})}{I_B} \qquad \text{(Eq. 3-7)}$$

where,
R_B is base bias resistance,
V_{CC} is supply voltage,
V_{BE} is base-emitter voltage,
V_{RE} is emitter-resistance voltage drop (emitter voltage),
I_B is the base current.

The other method brings to light an interesting characteristic of this circuit. Emitter resistor R_E is "reflected" back into the base circuit, multiplied by beta. In other words, the resistance from base to ground as far as an input signal (or the dc bias) is concerned appears to be 120 ohms × 40 = 4800 ohms, rather than 120 ohms. Thus, R_E can be used to increase the input impedance of the common-emitter amplifier.

To calculate R_B using this information, use the formula:

$$R_B = \frac{V_{CC} - V_{BE}}{I_B} - \beta \times R_E \qquad \text{(Eq. 3-8)}$$

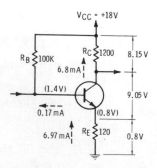

Fig. 3-8. Constructed circuit except for value of R_B.

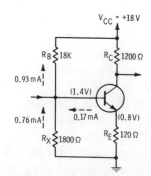

Fig. 3-9. Resistor R_X added to stabilize circuit.

The value for R_B will be the same in either case. The value of R_B for the circuit in Fig. 3-8 is $(18 - 0.6 - 0.8)/0.17$ mA $= 16.6$ V$/0.17$ mA (from equation 3-7), which is equal to 97.7K ohms. Using the nearest standard resistance value, make R_B 100K ohms.

This completes the design of a simple single-stage common-emitter amplifier. There are, however, many other bias circuits used to set the operating point of the transistor; most of them are considerably more stable than the simple bias method used throughout this example.

When the emitter current in the circuit tends to rise (whether due to changing temperature or leakage currents), the voltage drop across R_E will increase. If another resistor (R_X in Fig. 3-9) is added to the circuit from the base to ground, the voltage at the base will be held relatively constant when the emitter voltage tries to increase. The net result is a decrease in transistor forward bias that compensates for the current causing the attempted drifting of the circuit "Q" point (quiescent operating point).

Resistor R_X is usually chosen so that the current through it is two to six times larger than I_B. Four times I_B is a popular choice to bias the stage of Fig. 3-9. The value of R_B would be chosen to drop $V_{CC} - V_{BE} - V_{RE}$ volts at five times I_B, rather than just I_B as in Fig. 3-8. The value of R_X is then selected to draw four times I_B when $V_{BE} + V_{RE}$ is across it. In equation form:

$$R_B = \frac{V_{CC} - V_{BE} - V_{RE}}{5I_B} \qquad \text{(Eq. 3-9)}$$

and,

$$R_X = \frac{V_{BE} + V_{RE}}{4I_B} \qquad \text{(Eq. 3-10)}$$

For the circuit of Fig. 3-9, $R_B = 16.6$ V$/0.85$ mA $= 19.5$K ohms. The nearest standard value is 18K ohms. If this resistor is used, the current through it will be 0.93 mA, so the current through R_X should be $I_{RB} - I_B$ rather than four times I_B as shown in equation 3-10. Since $I_{RB} = 0.93$ mA and $I_B = 0.17$ mA, I_{RX} should be $0.93 - 0.17 = 0.76$ mA. The value of R_X should then be 1.4 V$/0.76$ mA $= 1840$ ohms, or 1800 ohms, since this is a standard resistor value.

Another method of bias stabilization is shown schematically in Fig. 3-10A. With this circuit, any increase in current causes the collector voltage to decrease, reducing the voltage across R_B and thereby reducing I_B and bringing I_C back to the quiescent point. The disadvantage in using this bias method is that the voltage gain of the circuit is reduced due to degenerative feedback from collector to base. This feedback can be eliminated (for ac signals) by using the circuit of Fig. 3-10B where C_B bypasses the signals to ground.

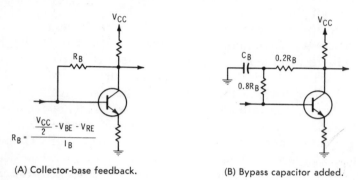

(A) Collector-base feedback.   (B) Bypass capacitor added.

Fig. 3-10. Two additional bias-stabilization methods.

Although the circuits shown so far will work, the effects of signal-source impedance, stage input impedance, stage output impedance, and load resistance have been ignored to simplify the discussion. The effects of all these things are covered in the chapter on multistage analog amplifiers, since it is when the stage is actually put to use in a system, that they become important.

THE COMMON-BASE CIRCUIT

The schematic for the common-base circuit configuration is shown in Fig. 3-11. This circuit has a low input impedance, a moderate output impedance, and provides voltage gain but no current gain. In contrast to the common-emitter circuit, the output signal from this circuit is in phase with the input signal. In actual practice, the circuit is not usually implemented in the way shown in Fig. 3-11 (using two supply sources). Except for dc-coupled applications, the circuit normally is constructed as shown in Fig. 3-12.

Capacitor C_B is used to bypass any signal at the base to common (ground) without affecting the dc bias point of the stage. Its value is chosen so that it appears as a very low impedance at the lowest signal frequency. (Calculating this value is discussed in Chapter 4.) This causes the base to be the common point as far as the input and output signals are concerned.

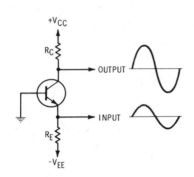

Fig. 3-11. Typical common-base circuit using two power-supply sources.

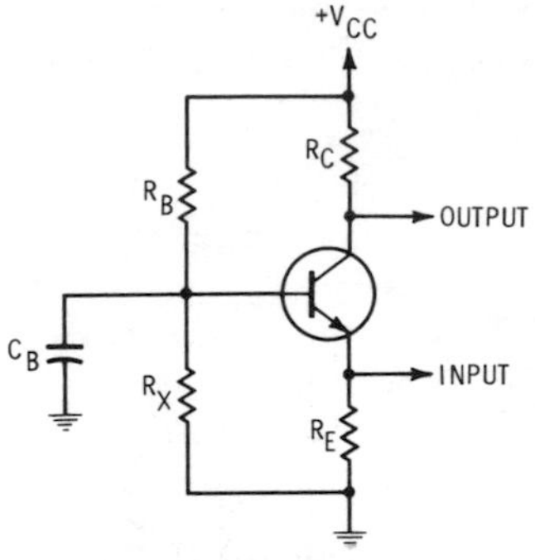

Fig. 3-12. Typical common-base circuit biased with one supply source.

When an input signal causes a change in the emitter voltage, a change in the base-emitter voltage is caused, and the base current (and therefore emitter current and collector current) changes. Where an increase in input voltage causes an increase in I_B in the common-emitter circuit, an increase in input voltage causes a decrease in I_B in the common-base circuit. This is why the signal is not inverted in the common-base configuration.

The common-base configuration is a good choice for a circuit when the impedance of the input signal source is low (such as a carbon microphone or a speaker) or when amplification without signal inversion is necessary.

The voltage gain in the common-base circuit is equal to the ratio of R_C to R_E, the same as in the common-emitter circuit. The current gain is always less than one, since the emitter current is equal to the input signal current, and the collector current, or output-signal current, is $I_E - I_B$. The actual current gain of the stage can be found if the value of beta is known. Beta is the ratio of collector current to base current ($\beta = I_C/I_B$). The Greek letter alpha (α) is used to denote the ratio of collector current to emitter current, ($\alpha = I_C/I_E$) and may be found using the formula:

$$\alpha = \frac{\beta}{\beta + 1} \qquad \text{(Eq. 3-11)}$$

The steps for designing a common-base amplifier circuit are the same as those required to design a common-emitter stage except for the additional requirement of C_B. The load line and quiescent bias point are the same regardless of circuit configuration.

THE COMMON-COLLECTOR CIRCUIT

The common-collector circuit, also called an emitter-follower circuit, is shown schematically in Fig. 3-13. This circuit has a high input impedance, a low output impedance, and good current gain but no voltage gain. An increase in the input signal voltage causes an increase in I_B. This increase results in an I_C increase of βI_B, which causes emitter current I_E to increase by $I_B + I_C$. This increased current causes a larger drop across R_E, which represents an increase in output signal voltage.

The common-collector circuit has a voltage gain of less than one, due to the degenerative feedback caused by the voltage being developed at the emitter. The actual voltage gain of the common-collector circuit is equal to alpha (α), which is the current gain of the transistor in the common-base circuit. Another way to determine why the voltage gain is less than one is to examine the voltage-gain equation, $A_V = R_C/R_E$, for the circuit of Fig. 3-13. In this circuit, R_C is replaced by a short circuit so that only the resistance in the collector of the transistor is available for the numerator of the equation. The collector re-

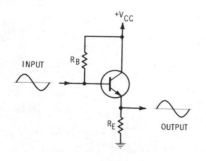

Fig. 3-13. Typical emitter-follower circuit.

sistance can be calculated from the formula $R_C = \alpha R_E$, and if this value is substituted into the voltage-gain equation,

$$A_V = \frac{\alpha R_E}{R_E} = \alpha$$

Since R_E in the common-collector circuit is always larger than R_C, the voltage gain of the stage is always less than one.

The input impedance of this circuit is usually very high, since (as mentioned in the section on the common-emitter circuit) R_E multiplied by beta is reflected back into the base circuit. If a transistor with a beta of 100 is used and R_E equals 1000 ohms, the input impedance of the transistor is 100×1000 ohms = 100K ohms.

The output impedance is low, since it is equal to R_E in parallel with the base resistance (R_B) reflected into the emitter. (When R_E is small compared to R_B/β, the output impedance is approximately equal to R_E.)

The design of an emitter follower differs from the design of the common-emitter and common-base circuits. Where those circuits were biased so that the collector voltage was approximately equal to $V_{CC}/2$, the emitter-follower should be biased so that the emitter voltage is approximately $V_{CC}/2$. This will allow the emitter voltage to swing from almost zero volts ($\approx V_{BE(sat)}$) to almost V_{CC} ($\approx V_{CC} - V_{CE(sat)}$). Alternatively, the stage may be biased so that the emitter voltage will never be required to go below zero volts.

Four examples (two correctly biased stages, one incorrectly biased stage, and one stage with unnecessarily high bias) are shown in Fig. 3-14 and should serve to illustrate the point at which the transistor should be biased. The circuits of Fig. 3-14A and Fig. 3-14B are biased correctly. The circuit of Fig. 3-14C is incorrectly biased; part of the input signal will not be reproduced. The circuit of Fig. 3-14D will function, but it dissipates much extra power in the transistor and in R_E. The circuit of Fig. 3-14B is preferred for small signals.

The actual circuit design is relatively simple. The supply voltage is specified the same as for a common-emitter circuit—approximately 150% of the peak-to-peak signal voltage. The value of R_E is then chosen in the same manner as $R_C + R_E$ was chosen in the common-emitter circuit. The required emitter voltage is specified and the base bias resistor value calculated.

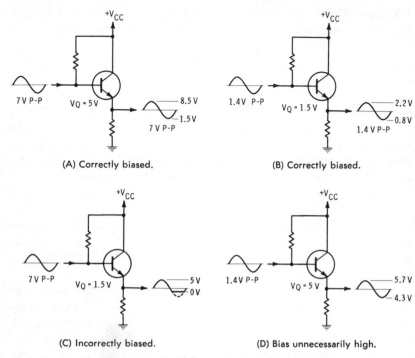

(A) Correctly biased.

(B) Correctly biased.

(C) Incorrectly biased.

(D) Bias unnecessarily high.

Fig. 3-14. Four emitter-follower circuits showing stage bias.

A practical emitter-follower circuit is shown in Fig. 3-15. The signal to be processed is a 10-volt peak-to-peak sine wave. Specify a 15-V power supply and calculate $I_{C(max)}$ as P_T/V_{CC}. In the circuit of Fig. 3-15, $I_{C(max)} = 0.3$ W/15 V = 20 mA. The resistance of R_E is then $V_{CC}/I_{C(max)} = 15$ V/0.02 A = 750 ohms, which is a standard resistor value.

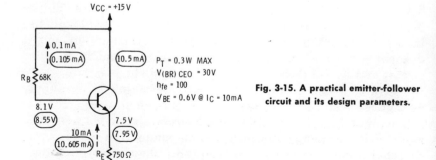

Fig. 3-15. A practical emitter-follower circuit and its design parameters.

Choose the quiescent emitter voltage equal to $V_{CC}/2$ in this circuit, so that the drop across R_E will be 7.5 V. This means that I_E will be 10 mA at the quiescent operating point. The value of I_B must then be approximately I_E/β, or 10 mA/100 = 0.1 mA. (There is a 1-percent error in this calculation since I_C, rather than I_E, equals βI_B, but it is of no consequence in this particular design. Actually, I_E equals $\beta I_B + I_B$, or $(\beta + 1)I_B$.)

The value of R_B is now calculated so that the voltage drop across it will be $V_{CC} - V_{BE} - V_{RE}$, or 6.9 V, when $I_B = 0.1$ mA. Therefore, $R_B = 6.9$ V/0.1 mA = 69,000 ohms. The nearest standard resistor value is 68K, and this should be used for R_B.

Once the component values are chosen as standard values, the circuit should be analyzed (as in Fig. 3-15) to make sure that it will function properly with those values. The circled values are not the design goals but the actual ones obtained after the design has been completed with standard components.

The common-collector circuit is useful for driving long lines or low-impedance loads. It is also useful anywhere a high-impedance source must be matched to a low-impedance load.

THE COMMON-SOURCE CIRCUIT

The common-source circuit configuration for the field-effect transistor (junction or insulated-gate) is analogous to the common-emitter circuit for bipolar transistors. It is the FET circuit configuration used most often, since it has good voltage gain coupled with a high input impedance.

Throughout the preceding discussion of bipolar transistors, the output current was related to the input current by α or β. The FET, however, is more of a voltage-operated device rather than a current-operated device. Its output current is related to its input voltage by y_{fs}, the forward transconductance of the device.

The basic common-source circuit is shown in Fig. 3-16. Since the junction FET is "on" when there is no gate voltage, the $-V_{GG}$ supply is used to reduce the drain current below I_{DSS}. (If this were not done, signals on the gate would be distorted tremendously rather than amplified at the drain terminal.) When an input signal is applied between the source and gate terminals, the voltage change at the gate causes the drain current,

I_D, to change. This causes a changing voltage drop across R_D, and the result is a replica of the input signal, 180° out of phase.

Biasing the junction FET using two power supplies, as in Fig. 3-16, is not the preferred method for two reasons: two power supplies cost twice as much as one, and, more importantly, there is no stabilization of the quiescent drain voltage with changes in temperature and transistor parameters (primarily I_{DSS}).

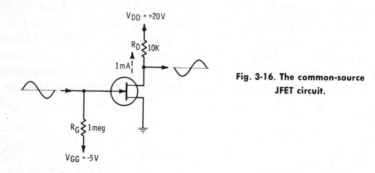

Fig. 3-16. The common-source JFET circuit.

A much more practical circuit is shown in Fig. 3-17. The addition of R_S to the circuit allows the use of one power supply and provides a measure of stabilization for I_D. The voltage developed across R_S is of the right polarity to reverse bias the gate so that I_D is reduced from I_{DSS} to the value selected for the stage. In addition, should I_D increase, the drop across R_S will increase, causing a larger voltage from gate to source and tending to reduce I_D. (This is the same effect as adding R_E in the bipolar circuit.) The value of R_S is determined, using Ohm's law, after the quiescent drain current is selected.

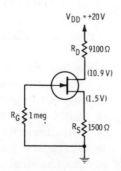

Fig. 3-17. R_S added to basic circuit to obtain self-bias.

To design the stage of Fig. 3-17, the following steps are taken:

1. Select the I_D that will exist in the circuit. This value will normally be about $\frac{1}{2} I_{DSS}$. The value of I_D at which y_{fs} is specified in the transistor characteristics is also usually a good choice and is probably about $\frac{1}{2} I_{DSS}$.
2. Specify the power-supply voltage as approximately 150 percent (or more) of the peak-to-peak voltage swing required at the drain terminal.
3. Calculate the value of R_S so that V_{GS} will be at the right value to maintain the quiescent I_D.
4. Calculate the value of R_D so that it will drop the correct amount of voltage at the quiescent I_D.
5. Calculate the voltage gain of the stage to determine the input voltage required to obtain the desired output.

Suppose a circuit is required that will provide a 13-V peak-to-peak signal using the transistor circuit and characteristics shown in Fig. 3-18. The supply voltage is specified as 150 percent of the 13-V peak-to-peak voltage swing at the drain, or 1.5×13 V $= 19.5$ V. Set the power supply equal to $+20$ volts dc.

To calculate the value for R_S that will cause the proper V_{GS} to be developed at I_D, the correct value of V_{GS} must be found first. This may be derived from the characteristic curves for the transistor by locating the intersection of the quiescent V_{DS} and quiescent I_D on the curve chart and extrapolating which value of V_{GS} will go through that point. It may be found more accurately using the formula:

$$V_{GS} = V_P \left(1 - \sqrt{\frac{I_D}{I_{DSS}}}\right) \qquad \text{(Eq. 3-12)}$$

where,
 V_{GS} is the gate-to-source voltage,
 V_P is the pinchoff voltage of the device,
 I_D is the required drain current,
 I_{DSS} is the specified I_D at $V_{GS} = 0$.

For the circuit of Fig. 3-18,

$$\begin{aligned}
V_{GS} &= 5 \left(1 - \sqrt{\frac{1}{2}}\right) \\
&= 5 \left(1 - 0.7\right) \\
&= 5 \times 0.3 \\
&= 1.5 \text{ volts}
\end{aligned}$$

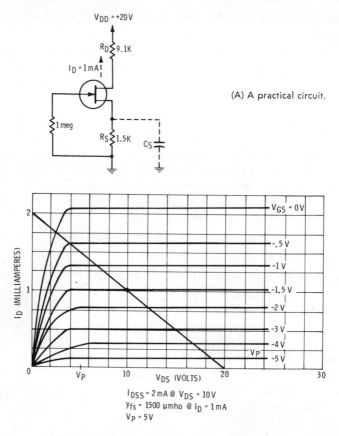

(A) A practical circuit.

(B) Circuit design parameters and characteristic curves.

Fig. 3-18. Designing the common-source JFET circuit.

If R_S is to drop 1.5 volts at 1 mA, it must be 1.5 V/1 mA = 1500 ohms.

For the voltage at the drain to swing symmetrically around the quiescent point, it must be set equal to one half the value of the supply voltage minus the drop across R_S or:

$$V_D = \frac{V_{DD} - V_{GS}}{2} = I_D R_D \qquad \text{(Eq. 3-13)}$$

First the quiescent I_D is chosen. In this case y_{fs} was specified at $I_D = 1$ mA and $I_{DSS}/2$ equals 1 mA, so this is a good choice of I_D. For our circuit, $V_D = (20 \text{ V} - 1.5 \text{ V})/2 = 9.25 \text{ V}$, so that R_D should be 9.25 V/1.0 mA = 9250 ohms. Since 9100 ohms is a standard value, it should be used. The error is negligible (around 1 percent in this case).

Finally, it is necessary to know the voltage gain of the stage. This may be approximated using the formula:

$$A_V = \frac{y_{fs} \times R_D}{1 + y_{fs}R_S} \qquad \text{(Eq. 3-14)}$$

For our circuit:

$$\begin{aligned}
A_V &= \frac{1500 \times 10^{-6} \text{ mho} \times 9.1 \times 10^3 \text{ ohms}}{1 + 1500 \times 10^{-6} \text{ mho} \times 1.5 \times 10^3 \text{ ohms}} \\
&= \frac{13,650 \times 10^{-3}}{1 + 2250 \times 10^{-3}} \\
&= \frac{13.65}{3.25} \\
&= 4.2
\end{aligned}$$

A different formula is used when R_S is shunted with a capacitor of such value that all signal voltage is bypassed to ground. This is shown by the dash connections to C_S in Fig. 3-18. The voltage gain for a stage with a bypassed R_S is approximately:

$$A_V = y_{fs}R_D \qquad \text{(Eq. 3-15)}$$

If C_S is used, the voltage gain of the circuit in Fig. 3-18 is 1500×10^{-6} mho $\times 9.1 \times 10^3$ ohm $= 13,650 \times 10^{-3} = 13.6$, more than three times the voltage gain without the bypass capacitor.

The input voltage required to obtain a 13-V peak-to-peak swing at the drain in the unbypassed version of the circuit is E_{out}/A_V, or 13 V/4.2 = 3.1 V peak-to-peak. This means that V_{GS} will go as low as $1.5 - 3.1/2 = -0.05$ V and as high as $1.5 + 3.1/2 = 3.05$ V. Reference to the characteristic curves shows that this range of input values is not allowable, since the device will saturate on positive signal peaks. A different circuit is needed.

When it is necessary to specify the voltage gain of the circuit in order to accommodate a given input-output signal swing, the circuit of Fig. 3-19 should be used. The value for $R_{S(total)}$ (the sum of R_{S1} and R_{S2}) is found in exactly the same way as R_S was previously found. Then R_{S1} is chosen using the formula

$$R_{S1} = \frac{y_{fs}R_D - A_V}{y_{fs}A_V}$$

where A_V is the specified required voltage gain. The resistance of R_{S2} is then $R_{S(total)} - R_{S1}$ and is bypassed so that it appears as a short to ac signals.

The common-source circuit and characteristic curves for the insulated-gate Type B field-effect transistor are shown in Fig. 3-20. This circuit is easier to design than the previous junction-FET circuit, since no gate bias need be used to set the operating point. The design steps are the same as for the JFET circuit except that the calculation of R_S is not needed. Of course, R_S can be used to help stabilize the operating point or to set the voltage gain of the stage.

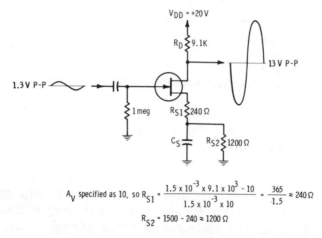

$$A_V \text{ specified as 10, so } R_{S1} = \frac{1.5 \times 10^{-3} \times 9.1 \times 10^3 - 10}{1.5 \times 10^{-3} \times 10} = \frac{365}{1.5} \approx 240\,\Omega$$

$$R_{S2} = 1500 - 240 \approx 1200\,\Omega$$

Fig. 3-19. Determination of resistances R_{S1} and R_{S2} for a specified A_V.

As with all transistor circuits, the other parameters mentioned in Chapter 2 should be considered so that the devices are never operated outside their maximum ratings. Also, the effects of source and load impedances on the circuits discussed have been ignored (as they were for the common-emitter bipolar circuit) to keep the design steps as simple as possible. These effects will be explored in the chapter on multistage analog amplifiers.

THE COMMON-GATE CIRCUIT

Diagrams of the common-gate FET circuit are shown in Fig. 3-21. Both the double and single power supply versions of

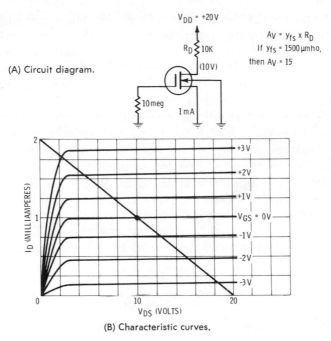

(A) Circuit diagram.

V_{DD} = +20V

R_D 10K

(10V)

$A_V = y_{fs} \times R_D$
If y_{fs} = 1500 μmho,
then A_V = 15

10 meg

1 mA

I_D (MILLIAMPERES)

+3 V
+2 V
+1 V
V_{GS} = 0V
-1 V
-2 V
-3 V

V_{DS} (VOLTS)

(B) Characteristic curves.

Fig. 3-20. The common-source circuit using an IGFET.

the common-gate bias circuit are shown. The circuit of Fig.
3-21B is the most common. Just as the bipolar common-base
circuit was biased in the same manner as the common-emitter
circuit, the FET common-gate circuit is biased in the same
way as the common-source circuit. The difference between
common-gate and common-source circuits lies in where the

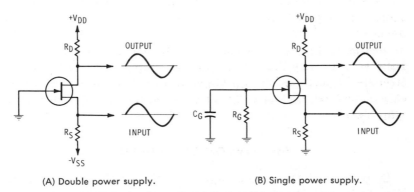

(A) Double power supply.

(B) Single power supply.

Fig. 3-21. Two versions of common-gate FET circuit.

input and output signals are referenced. The input impedance of the common-gate circuit is low, and the circuit exhibits a moderate output impedance. It has voltage gain but no current gain. The output signal is in phase with the input signal.

An input signal applied to the source terminal causes a change in the voltage from gate to source. If the input voltage increases, V_{GS} increases, I_D decreases, and the voltage at the drain increases. Exactly the opposite occurs when the input voltage decreases. Since the resistor in the drain circuit is usually larger than the resistor in the source circuit, a larger voltage is developed across R_D than across R_S for the same change in I_D (and therefore I_S). The result is a voltage gain. The current gain in a FET circuit is usually very close to one, since there is no gate current at any time. Therefore, the power gain is approximately equal to the voltage gain, which is:

$$A_V = \frac{y_{fs}R_D}{1 + y_{fs}R_S}$$

The common-gate configuration does not find widespread use since it does not take advantage of the field-effect transistor's most valuable parameter—high input impedance. It is used to some extent in rf amplifiers.

THE COMMON-DRAIN CIRCUIT

The common-drain circuit, or source follower as it is sometimes called, has a voltage gain of one. It does, however, have excellent current and power gain and a very high input impedance. Its operation is similar to the bipolar emitter-follower circuit.

The basic junction-FET source follower is shown schematically in Fig. 3-22. The design of the source follower requires only that the resistor in the source circuit develop a voltage, at quiescent drain current I_D, to hold I_D at approximately $I_{DSS}/2$. This requirement differs from the design of a bipolar emitter follower, where the emitter resistor could be chosen to drop one-half the supply voltage at any given I_C.

If R_S is too small, the stage will be operating too close to I_{DSS}. If R_S is too large, the stage will be operating too close to the pinch-off value of V_{GS}. For the circuit of Fig. 3-22, R_S

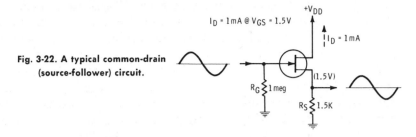

Fig. 3-22. A typical common-drain
(source-follower) circuit.

should be calculated exactly as it was for the common-source circuit. That is, R_S will drop V_{GS} at I_D, where

$$V_{GS} = V_P \left(1 - \sqrt{\frac{I_D}{I_{DSS}}} \right)$$

If the value of R_S that is selected in this fashion is incompatible with the output requirements of the circuit, its value may be either lowered or raised using the circuits shown in Figs. 3-23 and 3-24, respectively. The output impedance of the circuit is thereby adjusted to suit the specific circuit requirements without affecting the dc operation.

The insulated-gate FET common-drain circuit will normally require the extra bias resistor shown in Fig. 3-24 to maintain V_{GS} near the zero-volt point. A practical IGFET source follower is shown in Fig. 3-25. The voltage divider consisting of R_X and R_G maintains approximately 4.7 volts at the gate terminal. Since 4.7 volts is developed across R_S, the effective voltage from gate to source (V_{GS}) is zero.

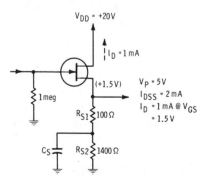

Fig. 3-23. A source-follower circuit biased
to lower the output impedance.

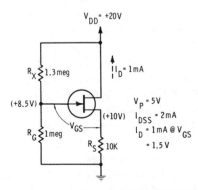

Fig. 3-24. A source-follower circuit biased
to raise the output impedance.

73

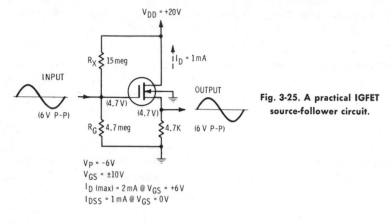

$V_{DD} = +20V$

R_X 15 meg

INPUT

$I_D = 1 mA$

(4.7 V)

OUTPUT

(6 V P-P)

(4.7 V)

R_G 4.7 meg   4.7K   (6 V P-P)

$V_P = -6V$
$V_{GS} = \pm 10V$
$I_{D\ (max)} = 2\,mA @ V_{GS} = +6V$
$I_{DSS} = 1\,mA @ V_{GS} = 0V$

Fig. 3-25. A practical IGFET source-follower circuit.

SUMMARY

The six basic solid-state circuits have been explored, and detailed design steps have been discussed for the two most useful configurations—the common-emitter bipolar circuit and the common-source FET circuit. As previously mentioned, the effects which the circuits connected to the input and output of a single-stage amplifier have on the operation of the amplifier have not been discussed. This would have complicated the designs so that the basic theory might have been lost in the details. Now that the fundamentals are thoroughly ingrained in the reader, these items will be discussed in the following chapter, where the individual circuits will be connected together to perform useful functions.

One other rather important area has also been ignored—the fact that transistor parameters (such as beta in bipolar circuits and I_{DSS} in FET circuits) are usually specified over a range of values, rather than at a specific point. These variations can have a tremendous effect on circuit performance. For example, if a circuit is designed around a transistor whose beta is assumed to be 50 but whose beta is actually 100, the collector current will be twice that required in the circuit. The transistor may even be saturated and the circuit will not operate.

Since parameters vary from device to device of the same type, each circuit will probably need some "fine tuning" on the bench once the basic design is completed. There are methods for stabilizing transistor operation for "worst-case" variations in all parameters. While these methods are used in most industrial applications where circuitry is mass produced, they are beyond the scope of this book. It is assumed that the reader is building one-of-a-kind (or few-of-a-kind) projects that lend themselves to optimization on the work bench. Even circuits that are checked with modern digital computers for "worst-case" conditions are built and tested on the bench before they are approved.

The reader who does not have a great familiarity with solid-state devices should design and build several different single-stage amplifiers and experiment with them. See what makes them work and what makes them perform improperly by changing resistor values and supply voltages (even transistors of the same type) to get a feel for circuit operation. It would be a worthwhile expenditure of time and effort.

CHAPTER 4

Multistage Analog Amplifiers

In order for a solid-state circuit to perform a useful function, it must be connected to a source and load, and usually to other circuits. Connecting anything to a single-stage circuit, including other single stages to create a multistage amplifier, changes the operation of that circuit. It is no longer isolated from the outside world, and the effects of its environment on its operation must be considered.

THE INPUT INTERFACE

The input impedance of a transistor stage has, in most cases, a marked effect on the gain of the stage, as illustrated in Fig. 4-1. Unless the source impedance is very low and the input impedance very high, a voltage-divider effect is created when the two are connected together.

If V_S in Fig. 4-1 is connected to a FET input stage, R_S can be ignored. However, should it be connected to a bipolar stage, such as the one shown in Fig. 4-2, the effect of R_S must be taken into account. The voltage divider consisting of R_S, R_B, R_X, and βR_E affects the output voltage of the stage. The capacitor is assumed to be a short circuit for the input signal, and its effect is ignored. To define exactly what effect the stage input impedance has on the overall circuit operation, the value of

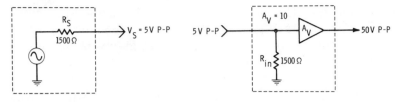

(A) Unloaded voltage source.

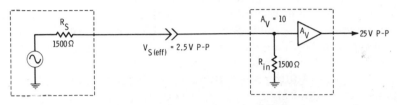

(B) Source loaded by following stage.

Fig. 4-1. Effect of source impedance on voltage gain.

the input impedance must be known. The input impedance of any stage is the parallel combination of all of the impedances connected to the input point. For the stage of Fig. 4-2, the input impedance is the parallel combination of R_B, R_X, and the value of R_E reflected into the base circuit (βR_E). Thus, for this circuit, $Z_{in} = 200K \| 20K \| (100 \times 200) =$ approximately 9000 ohms. (The symbol $\|$ means "in parallel with.") What effect does this have on V_{out}? If the source voltage is 5 V and the voltage gain of the stage is 10, we would expect V_{out} to be 50 V. However, since V_S (effective) is, in reality, no longer 5 V but

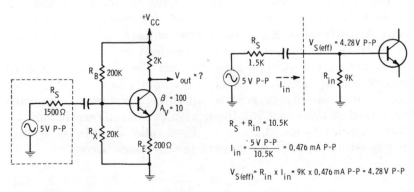

Fig. 4-2. Source connected to a bipolar transistor stage.

Fig. 4-3. Calculating $V_{S(eff)}$.

4.28 volts (see Fig. 4-3), $V_{out} = 42.8$ volts. This represents an actual stage voltage gain of 42.8/5, or 8.56, almost 15 percent less than the original calculated voltage gain. The voltage seen at the input is always less than the "unloaded" source voltage.

Why not make R_{in} as large as possible? For lowest noise and distortion, R_{in} should be within an "order of magnitude" (a factor of ten) of R_S. If the value of R_{in} is arbitrarily assigned a value of $5 \times R_S$, a rule of thumb can be developed for deciding upon the A_V required of a stage so that the output meets the requirements specified. Since $\frac{1}{6}$, or 17 percent, of the source voltage will be dropped across R_S if $R_{in} = 5 \times R_S$, the voltage gain of the stage should be 17 percent more than the "required" voltage gain. Adding a small margin for good measure, to compensate an input stage for the effects of R_S, make

$$A_V \text{ (actual)} = 1.2 \, A_V \text{ (desired)} \qquad \text{(Eq. 4-1)}$$

This will insure adequate voltage gain.

THE OUTPUT INTERFACE

In addition to the effects of the source and input impedances, there are two other factors affecting the voltage gain of a stage. These are the output impedance and load impedance. If a transistor stage is considered as the "input source" for the load impedance, it can be seen that the actual voltage gain of a stage is not exactly $A_V = R_C/R_E$ (as shown in Chapter 3) but is more complex to determine.

Fig. 4-4 illustrates the division of the output signal current (which determines the stage voltage gain) among the three output resistances. Since the actual voltage gain of the stage is the ratio of the voltage across the load resistance to the input voltage, the voltage-gain formula for the stage must be modified if an adequate A_V is to be maintained. Since the collector must supply current to all three resistances connected to it, rather than just R_C, the equivalent impedance in the collector circuit is R_C, R_O, and R_L in parallel. If this impedance is named $R_{L(ac)}$, the voltage gain for the stage becomes:

$$A_V = \frac{R_{L(ac)}}{R_E} \qquad \text{(Eq. 4-2)}$$

As stated above, $R_{L(ac)}$ in this equation is:

$$R_{L(ac)} = R_L || R_C || R_O \qquad \text{(Eq. 4-3)}$$

where,

$R_{L(ac)}$ is the equivalent output impedance in ohms,
R_L is the load (input to following stage) resistance in ohms,
R_C is the collector resistor in ohms,
R_O is the output resistor in ohms.

For the stage of Fig. 4-4, $R_{L(ac)} = 2K||50K||10K = $ approximately 1600 ohms. Therefore the voltage gain (Equation 4-2) is 1600 ohms/200 ohms = 8, when the stage is actually connected to its output load.

For the same reason that the input impedance to a stage was arbitrarily assigned a value of five times the source impedance (for an input stage), the collector resistor is usually assigned a value one-fifth the value of the load impedance (for an output stage). The value of R_O is usually neglected as such, and its effect is taken care of with a safety margin or "fudge factor."

The same 20-percent factor used with regard to A_V when compensating for R_S can be used to compensate A_V for the effect of R_L at the output. The voltage gain of the output stage (using just the value of R_C in the voltage gain equation) should be made equal to 1.2 A_V (desired) when $R_C = R_L/5$.

MULTISTAGE VOLTAGE GAIN

Using the rule-of-thumb factors just developed, it is possible to set the individual stage voltage gains to obtain the overall voltage gain in a multistage circuit without regard for the

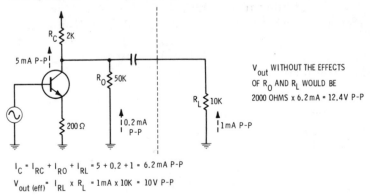

Fig. 4-4. Output loading of a transistor stage.

actual component values in the circuits. As long as each $R_{in} \cong 5R_S$ and each $R_C \cong R_L/5$, the A_V factor of 1.2 can be used as illustrated in Figs. 4-5 through 4-7. Note particularly that it is necessary to use the factor 1.2 only once at each stage interconnection, rather than twice. Compensating for R_S and R_L

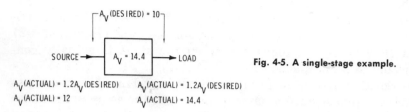

Fig. 4-5. A single-stage example.

at each connection point would result in a voltage gain greater than that actually required. When a single stage is used (Fig. 4-5), the output factor is multiplied by the desired voltage gain (obtained by multiplying the overall desired voltage gain by the input factor). When two stages are used (Fig. 4-6), the first stage is actually chosen to be the one with the highest A_V

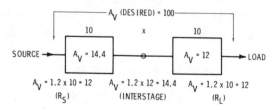

Fig. 4-6. A two-stage amplifier.

since it is not constrained by R_L. In Fig. 4-7, stage one was compensated both for the effect of R_S and for the effect of stage two acting as R_L. In any case, the factor 1.2 is used $n + 1$ times, where n is the number of single stages. In this case, with three stages, the factor 1.2 is used four times.

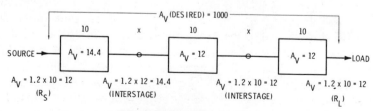

Fig. 4-7. A three-stage amplifier.

While all of this is suitable for a hypothetical multistage design whose parameters are easily controlled, the design of a multistage analog amplifier can be done much more accurately with the actual component values. These previous examples were presented to show the "why" of the steps taken in the following actual design example.

A MULTISTAGE DESIGN EXAMPLE

Suppose that we need a "system" that will provide a minimum of 10 mW of audio signal to a 5000-ohm load in response to an input stimulus whose output is 100 mV p-p of signal when feeding an $R_{in} = R_s = 10,000$ ohms over the frequency range of 100 Hz to 10,000 Hz. Since the input and output parameters are in different units, the first step should be the definition of the system stimulus-response requirements. This is illustrated in Fig. 4-8.

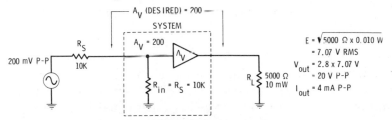

Fig. 4-8. Defining the system parameters.

The system must have a voltage gain of 20 V/0.1 V = 200. This value cannot be obtained easily with one stage, so it appears that when the block diagram is created, at least two stages must be used. The input impedance of the system should be at least 10,000 ohms (but less than 100,000 ohms) if the source is to deliver adequate signal to it. A suitable block diagram is shown in Fig. 4-9. The system gain must be divided up between the two stages. Assuming the use of common-emitter stages, the value of R_E in stage two should be kept large for good stability. Since the output impedance is low, the value of the stage-two emitter resistor must remain small if adequate gain is to be maintained. Where is the crossover point? In a two-stage amplifier, the gain of the first stage is usually made two to four times the gain of the second stage. If we chose the gain of the second stage as 8, the gain of the first stage can be roughly three times that, or 25, which is not an unobtainable goal, and the product equals 200, the required system A_V.

The circuit function for both stages is that of an amplifier, and the concluding sentence of the previous paragraph constitutes an analysis of the design. The system should work when the circuits are designed. The actual circuit design can proceed very logically from output to input. The circuit configuration is shown in Fig. 4-10. For the moment, ignore the three coupling capacitors. Their values will be calculated as the last step in the design.

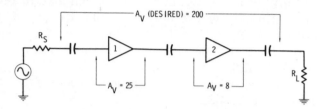

Fig. 4-9. Block diagram of a two-stage analog amplifier.

We know that 20 V p-p is required across R_L, which is 5000 ohms. If we make $R_{C2} = R_L/5$, $R_{C2} = 1000$ ohms (which is a standard value). The value of $R_{L(ac)}$ is then R_{C2} in parallel with R_L, or $5000 \times 1000/(5000 + 1000) = 833$ ohms. For the voltage gain of stage 2 to be equal to 8, R_{E2} must equal $R_{L(ac)}/A_V = 833$ ohms$/8 = 104$ ohms. Use 100 ohms since it is the nearest standard value. The supply voltage can now be calculated. A minimum of 20 V p-p is required across R_{C2}, and a minimum of 2.5 V p-p is required across R_{E2}. Allowing at least 3 V across

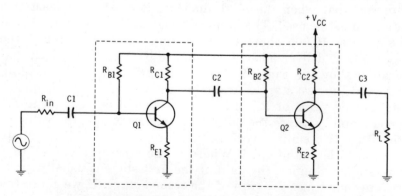

Fig. 4-10. Circuit components arranged as actual circuitry.

the transistor, V_{CC} must be at least 25.5 V dc. Adding a safety factor ($\cong$25 percent) of about 6.5 V, make $V_{CC} = 32$ V dc.

Resistor $R_{C2} = 1000$ ohms and $R_{E2} = 100$ ohms so that with $V_{CC} = 32$ V, $I_{C(max)} = 29$ mA. The maximum power dissipation of the stage is at the quiescent point and will be $V_{CE} \times I_C$. Since $V_{CE} = V_{CC}/2$ and $I_C = I_{C(max)}/2$, the maximum power is $V_{CE} \times I_C = 16$ V $\times$ 14.5 mA = 0.23 watt. A transistor with a dissipation rating in excess of 0.5 W should work adequately. The 2N2897 transistor is a good choice for this application. Its characteristics are listed in Fig. 4-11, along with the circuit parameters of stage two of the design. The value of $I_{C(max)}$ for stage two is 29 mA, so $I_{C(Q)}$ should be $I_{C(max)}/2 = 14.5$ mA. With the typical beta of 100, $I_{B(Q)}$ will be 14.5/100 = 0.145 mA. The voltage at the emitter will be (14.5 mA + 0.145 mA) $\times$ 100 ohms = 1.46 V. The voltage at the base will be approximately 2 V. Resistor $R_{B2} = (32$ V $- 2$ V)/0.145 mA = 30 V/0.145 mA = 207,000 ohms, or 207K. Use 200K, the nearest standard value.

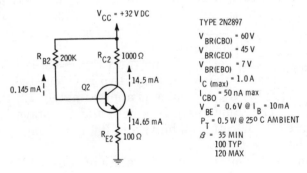

Fig. 4-11. Quiescent condition for stage 2.

Once all the resistor values are calculated, the input impedance of stage two can be calculated. It is R_{B2} in parallel with the value of R_{E2} times beta or 200K$||$(100 ohms $\times$ 100) = 9500 ohms. This 9500 ohms represents the load resistance for stage one, as shown in Fig. 4-12.

If R_{C1} is made approximately 9500/5, or 2000 ohms, R_{E1} must be less than 70 ohms for a stage voltage gain of 25. Since this value of R_{E1} is rather small, make R_{C1} equal to one-half the stage two input impedance (rather than one-fifth of it), or 4700 ohms. The stage-one $R_{L(ac)}$ is now 4700$||$9500, or approximately 3000 ohms. For a stage gain of 25, R_{E1} will be 3000/

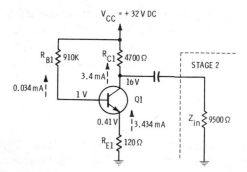

Fig. 4-12. Resistor values for stage 1.

25 = 120 ohms, a standard value. The $I_{C(max)}$ is 32 V/4820 ohms = 6.6 mA, so $I_{C(Q)}$ should be 3.3 mA. The quiescent collector voltage will then be 16.5 V, and 0.4 volt will be dropped across R_{E1}. The magnitude of I_B should be set to 0.033 mA by R_{B1}. Therefore, $R_{B1} = (V_{CC} - V_{BE} - V_{RE})/I_B = (32\ V - 0.6\ V - 0.4\ V)/0.033\ mA = 31\ V/0.033\ mA = 940K$. The nearest standard value is 910K, which will provide an I_B of 0.034 mA. The input impedance to stage one is $910K||(100 \times 120\ ohms) = 910K||12K =$ approximately 11.9K, perfectly adequate for the input source resistance specified.

The final circuit version is shown in Fig. 4-13. It is interesting to note that if the A_V of stage two is calculated from the formula $A_V = R_C/R_E$, the value is approximately 1.2 times the desired A_V. The same analysis is not valid for stage one since we modified it for better stability and R_{C1} is no longer one-fifth of R_L (the stage-two Z_{in}).

The only items missing are the values of the coupling capacitors. The rule of thumb for coupling capacitors is to choose

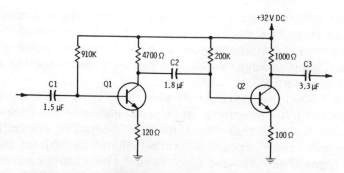

Fig. 4-13. Final version of amplifier circuit showing component values.

their value so that the X_C of the capacitor at the lowest expected frequency is less than one-tenth the value of the input impedance that the capacitor is feeding. Table 4-1 shows the values for C1, C2, and C3 in the circuit just designed. The formula for C is:

$$C \geqq \frac{10}{2\pi f Z_{in}}$$

where,
   C is the desired capacitance in farads,
   10 is a numerical constant to reduce X_C to one-tenth of Z_{in},
   2π is a constant,
   f is the lowest frequency (in hertz) to be coupled,
   Z_{in} is the impedance in ohms of the stage to be coupled to.

The example just described was designed to show the interaction of source and load impedances in multistage amplifier design on the input, the output, the interstage interface, and the overall voltage gain. With some practice and experience, this type of design will become an easy task.

Table 4-1. Values for Coupling Capacitors in Fig. 4-13, Calculated for Frequency of 100 Hz

Stage	Z_{in}	$X_C \leqq 0.1\,Z_{in}$	$C \geqq$	C
1	11.9K	1.19K	1.34 μF	1.5 μF (C1)
2	9.5K	0.95K	1.67 μF	1.8 μF (C2)
R_L	5.0K	0.5 K	3.2 μF	3.3 μF (C3)

INTERSTAGE COUPLING METHODS

There are many methods for coupling the output signal of one stage into the input of the following stage. The only method used so far has been capacitive coupling. There are two other coupling methods in practical use—transformer coupling and direct (or dc) coupling.

Transformer coupling is useful wherever an impedance match (either up or down) is required without an additional active stage and whenever isolation between two stages (or even two systems) is required, since there is no electrical connection between primary and secondary. Transformer coupling is relatively simple to use at input, interstage, or output interface points. However, it might be worthwhile to discuss some transformer parameters before investigating the actual circuitry.

The basic transformer is shown in Fig. 4-14. The ratio of the number of turns in the primary winding of the transformer to the number of turns in the secondary winding is called the turns ratio (T) of the transformer. (In equation form, $T = N_{pri}/N_{sec}$.) The output (secondary) voltage is equal to the input (primary) voltage divided by the turns ratio, ignoring transformer losses. The secondary current equals T times the primary current, and the power in each winding is the same (again ignoring losses). The impedance of the secondary is equal to the impedance of the primary divided by T^2. The only parameters that are not strictly tied to the turns ratio are the primary and secondary dc resistances, although they may be in nearly the same ratio as N_{pri}/N_{sec}. The losses that we have been ignoring are primarily a function of the dc resistances of the windings (although there are some losses due to the core and the currents in the windings). The dc resistance of the windings causes a power loss, since the resistance contributes nothing to the transformer action but it does dissipate power in the form of heat. For most small-signal applications, however, these losses may be ignored.

Transformer coupling of an input source to the input of a stage is illustrated in Fig. 4-15. The circuit of Fig. 4-15A may be used if the V_{BE} of the transistor is low enough and the dc resistance of the secondary is high enough to allow for proper dc biasing of the stage. Capacitor C1 in Fig. 4-15B allows the transistor to be biased regardless of the dc resistance of the secondary of T1. The primary design consideration in these circuits is the selection of the transformer so that its input impedance is equal to the source impedance. The turns ratio

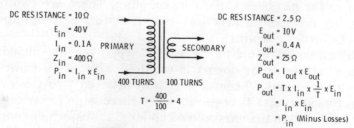

Fig. 4-14. Parameter relationships in a transformer.

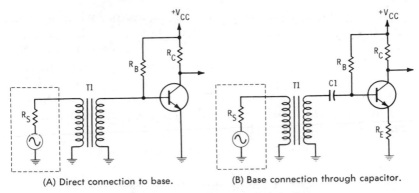

(A) Direct connection to base. (B) Base connection through capacitor.

Fig. 4-15. Two transformer-coupled circuits.

and output impedance are not nearly as important unless the characteristics of the transistor stage cannot be modified to accommodate any transformer.

Using a transformer as an interstage or output coupling device is considerably more complex, since the selection of the transformer affects the design of the driving (and sometimes driven) stage. A single example (Fig. 4-16) should serve to illustrate driver (and driven) stage design. The driven stage can be replaced by the ultimate load if the transformer is to be used as an output coupling device, and the driver stage can be replaced by the input source if the transformer is to be used as an input coupling device.

Suppose that we need to drive a stage whose input impedance is 250 ohms (this corresponds to the transformer load) and that the load impedance of the driver stage is to be 4000 ohms. Since $T = N_{pri}/N_{sec} = \sqrt{Z_{pri}/Z_{sec}}$, the turns ratio for this transformer must be $\sqrt{4000/250} = \sqrt{16/1} = 4/1$. Assume that the transformer selected has dc resistances as shown in Fig. 4-16.

A 0.4-V p-p signal is available as input to the first stage, and 1 V p-p must be delivered to the second stage. If a 25-percent allowance for losses (a good rule of thumb) is included, 5 V p-p must be developed across the primary of the transformer. The primary impedance of the transformer is the collector load, R_C, for stage one. For 5 V p-p across 4000 ohms, the collector signal current must be 1.25 mA p-p. If the collector current of Q1 is set to 2 mA, it can easily swing from 1.375 mA to 2.625 mA, the required peak-to-peak current swing. Since 0.4-V p-p is available as input signal and the collector swing must be 5 V, the A_V of the stage should be 5 V/0.4 V = 12.5, and R_E must then be 4000 ohms/12.5 = 320 ohms or less. Choose the next lowest standard value, 300 ohms. If we assume the beta of Q1 to be 100, $R_{B1} = (V_{CC} - V_{BE} - R_E I_E)/I_B = (9\ V - 0.6V - 0.6V)/0.02\ mA = 7.8\ V/0.02\ mA = 390K$, a standard value. The first stage has now been designed around the transformer and biased to operate properly.

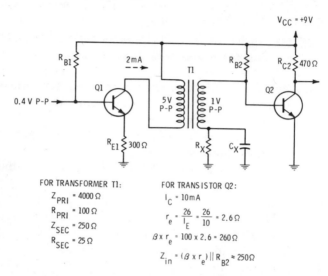

Fig. 4-16. Interstage transformer coupling with circuit parameters listed.

It should be noted that there are actually two load lines for Q1 in Fig. 4-16—an ac load line using $R_C + R_E = Z_{pri} + R_E = 4300$ ohms, and a dc load line constructed from $R_{pri} + R_E$. The ac load line is the path that I_C will take as long as the circuit is operating properly. Should the input be overdriven or raised to a dc level above the bias point, collector current limited only by R_{pri} and R_E will flow, resulting in nonlinear stage operation. The end result is distortion and/or possible over-dissipation in Q1, so care should be taken to prevent these conditions.

What about the design of the Q2 stage? The Z_{sec} must be used as the source impedance to calculate the Q2 stage voltage gain. An amount equal to R_{sec} must be subtracted from R_X if proper bias is to be maintained, although this value is usually negligible. Resistor R_X is necessary if the calculated value for

R_X is larger than R_{sec} and if proper bias cannot be obtained using $R_X = R_{sec}$. Capacitor C_X is used to bypass signal variations to ground, so that the input signal is developed only across the secondary winding and not current-limited by R_X.

Besides capacitive and transformer coupling, the third coupling method in general use is direct, or dc coupling. Direct coupling has the advantage of not requiring a separate component to effect the coupling of an output to an input. The two points are simply connected together. The primary disadvantages of dc coupling are the difficulty of design and the difficulty in maintaining stability. Stability is difficult to maintain in a dc-coupled circuit because any small change in the operating point of the first stage is amplified by all subsequent stages. However, dc coupling is a particularly useful method when only two stages are concerned.

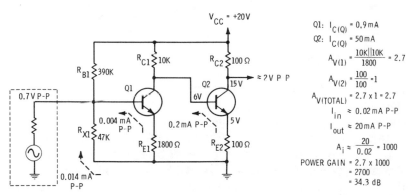

Fig. 4-17. A direct-coupled circuit with circuit parameters listed.

The dc coupling of two npn common-emitter stages is shown in Fig. 4-17. Although the voltage gain of the circuit is low, the current gain is very high, resulting in an excellent power gain. Overall gain could be further increased by raising R_{B1} and R_{X1} at the expense of circuit stability. The circuit operation is relatively straightforward. Transistor Q1 is biased to maintain an I_B of 0.5 mA into βR_{E2} (the Q2 input resistance). Changes in the I_C of Q1 cause corresponding (but opposite) changes in the I_B of Q2. The result is an almost steady voltage at the collector of Q1; even though the ratio of current through Q1 and Q2 is constantly changing, one rises while the other falls, and the current through R_{C1} is almost constant.

This circuit is difficult to design because of the difference between the usual desired voltage at the collector of Q1 and the usual desired voltage at the base of Q2. In the circuit of Fig. 4-17, it was necessary to raise R_{E2} to a value equal to R_{C2} just to raise the base voltage of Q2 to a value compatible with proper operation of transistor Q1, resulting in $A_V = 1$ for the Q2 stage.

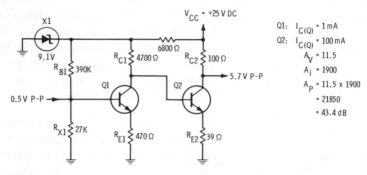

Fig. 4-18. Use of zener diode to obtain second power source.

If two separate power supplies of different voltages are available, it is easier to bias stage one so that $V_{CE} = V_{CC1}/2$ is approximately the same value as $V_{BE2} + V_{RE2}$. This eases the voltage-gain restriction mentioned earlier. An example of this, implemented with a zener diode rather than two separate power supplies, is shown in Fig. 4-18. By using diode X1, we allow the stages to be designed individually for both voltage gain and current gain. The overall power gain is then considerably increased.

Two additional ways to use the zener diode in direct-coupled circuits are shown in Figs. 4-19 and 4-20. With the configuration of Fig. 4-19, the base voltage of stage two is raised to a value compatible with the collector voltage of stage one. In Fig. 4-20, the zener is used effectively to eliminate the difference between the two voltage levels. The effective V_{CC} for stage two in Fig. 4-19 is about 11 volts. If a large output signal swing is necessary, this circuit is not as good as the circuit of Fig. 4-20.

With the configuration of Fig. 4-20, R_{X2} may not be necessary if the current levels are high enough to prevent the zener current from going below I_K.

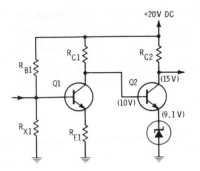

Fig. 4-19. Use of zener diode in
emitter circuit.

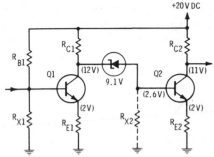

Fig. 4-20. Use of zener diode in base circuit
to eliminate a potential difference.

DIRECT-COUPLED COMPLEMENTARY STAGES

As mentioned in a previous chapter, there are times when using strictly npn or pnp transistors (or all n-channel or p-channel FET's, for that matter) is not the best choice. Direct-coupled circuits lend themselves very well to using complementary pairs (one pnp, one npn).

Three examples of this type of circuit are shown in Figs. 4-21, 4-22, and 4-23. It should be noted that here, as in all dc-coupled circuits, the supply voltage is normally a much larger value than the expected output signal swing. The reason for this is that much of the V_{CC} supply is "eaten up" by the zeners and resistors necessary to maintain proper operating-point bias. The total of all voltage drops in the circuit must be added

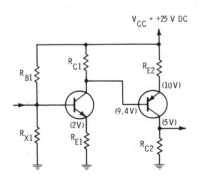

Fig. 4-21. A direct-coupled complementary
circuit with normal limitations of a dc-
coupled circuit.

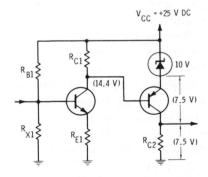

Fig. 4-22. A direct-coupled complementary
circuit to overcome voltage-
gain restriction.

to the output signal swing before the V_{CC} supply can be specified. The circuit of Fig. 4-21 has basically the same limitations as all dc-coupled circuits. The circuit of Fig. 4-22 overcomes the voltage-gain restriction, while the circuit of Fig. 4-23 both overcomes the voltage gain restriction and allows a larger signal swing.

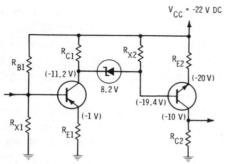

Fig. 4-23. A direct-coupled complementary circuit permitting a larger signal swing and overcoming voltage-gain restriction.

FEEDBACK

Feedback results when a portion of the output signal of a circuit is returned (or fed back) to the input of that circuit. Feedback can be either planned and utilized well or ignored with a resulting degradation of circuit performance. An example of the result of unplanned feedback is the howl or screech that results in a p-a system when the microphone is too close to the speaker. The resulting feedback from speaker (output) to microphone (input) causes the system to oscillate.

Feedback is of two types—positive, or regenerative, and negative, or degenerative. Each of these two types may be further classified as either voltage feedback or current feedback. Feedback may be applied in series with the input or in parallel (shunt) with the input.

Positive, or regenerative, feedback tends to add to, or reinforce, the input signal, increasing the gain of an amplifier. When the positive feedback is great enough, it converts the amplifier into an oscillator. Extensive use is made of positive feedback in signal-source applications, so the discussion of this topic is left for that chapter.

Negative, or degenerative, feedback tends to subtract from, or reduce the effect of, the input signal, decreasing the gain of an amplifier, even to the point where the output is equal to or less than the input. Negative feedback does more than simply decrease the gain of an amplifier. It increases the bandwidth (the frequency range that the amplifier will handle) since, as the amplifier output tends to decrease, the signal returned to the input tends to decrease. The end result is that the output signal size with a given input signal size tends to remain constant over a wider frequency range than it would in an amplifier without feedback. Another effect of negative feedback is to reduce the noise at the output of an amplifier. Since the noise is also returned, its value is reduced by the same ratio as the signal. Note that negative feedback will not, however, change the ratio of signal to noise—just their absolute values.

Perhaps the simplest example of negative feedback is the ordinary common-emitter amplifier illustrated in Fig. 4-24. This type of feedback is known as voltage feedback of the series type. The current through R_E in Fig. 4-24A causes the "feedback network" in Fig. 4-24B to look like a voltage source

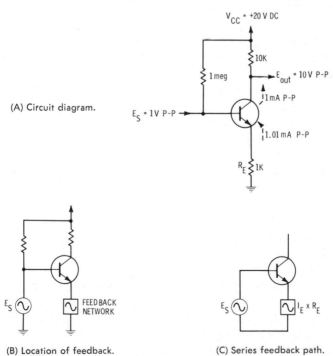

(A) Circuit diagram.

(B) Location of feedback.

(C) Series feedback path.

Fig. 4-24. Example of negative feedback in common—emitter amplifier.

of the same instantaneous polarity as the input source. The path from input to output of the network of Fig. 4-24C is a series path. The net result is that the voltage $(I_E \times R_E)$ in series with the input (E_S) reduces the effect of the input voltage change. Thus, a common-emitter amplifier with R_E installed has less voltage gain than one without an external R_E. How much voltage gain does it have? The general equation for the voltage gain in any feedback circuit is:

$$A_{Vf} = \frac{A_V}{1 - fA_V} \qquad \text{(Eq. 4-4)}$$

where,

A_{Vf} is the voltage gain with feedback,
A_V is the voltage gain without feedback,
f is the portion of the output signal returned to the input.

The sign of f is − for negative feedback and + for positive feedback.

For the circuit of Fig. 4-24, the portion of the output voltage used as feedback is:

$$
\begin{aligned}
f &= \frac{I_E R_E}{I_E R_E + I_C R_C} \\
&= \frac{1.01 \text{ mA} \times 1000 \text{ }\Omega}{1.01 \text{ mA} \times 1000 \text{ }\Omega + 1 \text{ mA} \times 10{,}000 \text{ }\Omega} \\
&= \frac{1.01 \text{ V}}{11 \text{ V}} \\
&= 0.09
\end{aligned}
$$

Assuming that the voltage gain of the circuit without feedback is equal to the beta of the transistor, or 100, the voltage gain with feedback is:

$$
\begin{aligned}
A_{Vf} &= \frac{A_V}{1 - f(A_V)} \\
&= \frac{100}{1 - (-0.09)(100)} \\
&= \frac{100}{1 + 9} \\
&= 10
\end{aligned}
$$

which agrees with our previous calculation of $A_V = R_C/R_E = 10$.

It should be noted that the application of voltage feedback has little or no effect on the current gain of the circuit. Similarly, the application of current feedback has little effect on the voltage gain of the circuit.

Fig. 4-25 illustrates the block diagram for any amplifier and feedback network. This block diagram represents the general case, rather than any specific circuit (such as the one just discussed). The overall gain of an amplifier with feedback can be calculated (or planned) by representing the circuits in the form of this block diagram. Voltage feedback results when a sample of the output voltage is applied to the input of an amplifier. When voltage feedback is applied in series with the input of the amplifier, the output impedance of the amplifier decreases to

$$Z_{of} = \frac{Z_O}{1 - fA_V} \qquad \text{(Eq. 4-5)}$$

and the input impedance increases to

$$Z_{If} = Z_I(1 - fA_V) \qquad \text{(Eq. 4-6)}$$

Voltage feedback in shunt with the input reduces both the output and input impedances. Examples of single-stage shunt feedback and two-stage series voltage feedback are shown in Figs. 4-26 and 4-27 respectively.

The formula shown in Fig. 4-27,

$$A_{Vf} = \frac{A_V(E_{in})}{E_{in} - f(E_{out})} \qquad \text{(Eq. 4-7)}$$

where A_V is the product of all the voltage gains without feedback in a multistage circuit, is used instead of the basic feedback formula (Equation 4-4). A different formula is required because the effect of these voltage gains is to change the amount of voltage fed back to the input, regardless of what the value of f is.

It is important to remember that when series feedback is used, the output point from which the feedback voltage is taken must be in phase with the input point to which the feedback voltage is applied. With shunt feedback, the output point from which the feedback voltage is taken must provide a signal 180° out of phase with the signal at the amplifier input to which the feedback voltage is to be applied.

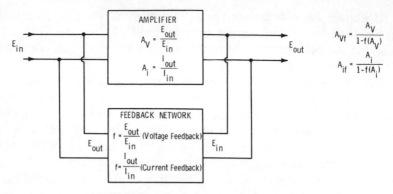

Fig. 4-25. Block diagram of basic feedback amplifier.

Current feedback is used primarily in dc-coupled circuits. In addition to the effects of negative feedback mentioned earlier, feedback also reduces the variations in the total gain of the circuit over which it is applied. With negative current feedback, the end result is the stabilization of the operating point and current gain of the circuit. Changes in current gain are reduced to:

$$\Delta A_{If} = \frac{A_{If}}{A_I\left(\dfrac{\Delta A_I}{1 - fA_I}\right)} \qquad \text{(Eq. 4-8)}$$

An example of shunt current feedback around a two-stage dc-coupled audio-frequency amplifier is shown schematically in Fig. 4-28. Capacitor C_B is used to bypass ac signal variations to

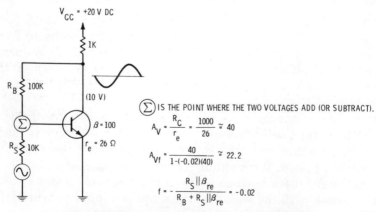

Fig. 4-26. An example of single-stage shunt feedback.

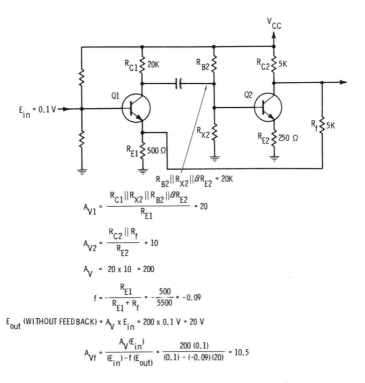

$$R_{B2} \| R_{X2} \| \beta R_{E2} = 20K$$

$$A_{V1} = \frac{R_{C1} \| R_{X2} \| R_{B2} \| \beta R_{E2}}{R_{E1}} = 20$$

$$A_{V2} = \frac{R_{C2} \| R_f}{R_{E2}} = 10$$

$$A_V = 20 \times 10 = 200$$

$$f = -\frac{R_{E1}}{R_{E1} + R_f} = -\frac{500}{5500} = -0.09$$

$$E_{out} \text{ (WITHOUT FEEDBACK)} = A_V \times E_{in} = 200 \times 0.1 \, V = 20 \, V$$

$$A_{Vf} = \frac{A_V (E_{in})}{(E_{in}) - f (E_{out})} = \frac{200 \, (0.1)}{(0.1) - (-0.09)(20)} = 10.5$$

Fig. 4-27. An example of two-stage series voltage feedback.

ground, even though in current feedback circuits the voltage gain in the circuit is not affected, unless the feedback is very large. Resistor R_f is used to provide bias current to the base of transistor Q1. Should the collector current of Q1 increase (due to signal current or changes in I_{CBO}), the collector current of Q2 will decrease. A decrease in current through Q2 means less voltage developed across R_{E2}. Since the I_B of Q1 is supplied from the voltage across R_{E2}, when this voltage decreases, the base current of Q1 tends to decrease. This, in turn, decreases the collector current of Q1 and compensates for the original increase in the collector current of Q1 that began the chain of events. This action stabilizes the circuit quiescent bias conditions and the overall circuit gain, which is:

$$A_{If} = \frac{A_I \times I_{in}}{I_{in} - fI_{out}} \qquad \text{(Eq. 4-9)}$$

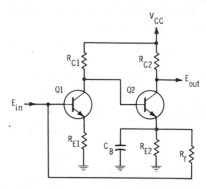

Fig. 4-28. Shunt-type current feedback in a two-stage dc-coupled af amplifier.

The voltage gain of the circuit may be calculated by the methods developed earlier in this chapter.

The use of negative feedback in an amplifier may tend to make the amplifier unstable, however, if the feedback is not negative at all frequencies where the system gain is greater than one. For example, since there is a phase shift through each capacitor in a capacitively coupled circuit, it is possible for the sum of the phase shifts to equal 180° at some frequency, turning the amplifier into an oscillator at that frequency. There is a slight phase shift through each active component (transistor) that may also contribute to this problem.

The cure? The design of any amplifier with voltage feedback must ensure that the overall gain of the system is less than unity ($A_v < 1$ with voltage feedback) at and above the frequency where the overall phase shift through the amplifier exceeds about 150°. One method for insuring that the overall voltage gain will be less than one is to place a capacitor in the feedback network to bypass unwanted positive feedback above

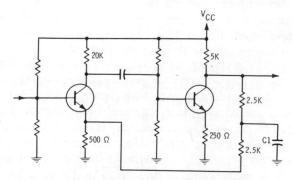

Fig. 4-29. Stabilization of a feedback amplifier.

the desired frequency range of the amplifier. Capacitor C1 in Fig. 4-29 serves this purpose. Alternately, a capacitor may be placed across the feedback network in some circuits to provide a large amount of negative feedback to prevent oscillation.

In many feedback circuits, the capacitor in the feedback network may not be necessary. Proper selection of coupling devices and careful construction practice should help to keep instability and oscillation at a minimum. Each circuit should be tested to be sure that it is stable.

POWER AMPLIFIER CIRCUITS

No discussion of multistage analog amplifiers would be complete without mentioning power amplifier circuits. Power amplifiers are necessary for driving speakers in audio applications, for driving motors in servo applications, and in other applications where small signals (as discussed thus far) are inadequate to drive the ultimate load.

Amplifiers are divided into several classes. Class A refers to circuits in which there is current through the active device during all portions of the signal swing; class B refers to circuits in which there is current through the active device during one half of the signal swing; class C refers to circuits in which there is current through the active device during less than half of the signal swing. There are also combinational classes, such as class AB, in which there is current through the active device for more than one half but less than all of the signal swing. Perhaps the simplest power circuit is the class-A transformer-coupled circuit. An output power amplifier stage of this type is shown in Fig. 4-30.

The class-A stage has poor efficiency (50 percent at best). This is because power equal to $V_{CC}/2$ times $I_{C(max)}/2$ is dissipated during most of the output signal swing.

The design of a power stage usually starts with the specification of the output power required. Suppose, in Fig. 4-30, that one watt is the required power that must be supplied to R_L. If 25 percent is added to this for transformer losses, 1.25 watts must be provided by the transistor stage. The device must, therefore, be capable of dissipating 2.5 watts (50 percent to the load and 50 percent in the circuit itself). A suitable transistor for this application is the 2N3418 (with a heat sink).

It can easily dissipate 2.5 watts, and it has an $I_{C(max)}$ rating of 3 amperes and a $V_{BR(CEO)}$ of 60 volts.

If we choose $I_{C(max)}$ in our circuit as 1.5 A, $I_{C(Q)}$ will be 0.75 A, and the collector current can swing from approximately 0.2 A to 1.3 A (taking into account the effects of I_{CBO} and $V_{CE(sat)}$). The rms value of this swing is $0.707 \times I$ p-p$/2 = 0.707 \times 1.1/2 = 0.39$ A. In order to deliver 1.25 W to the transformer, the rms voltage required across the transformer primary is $E = 1.25$ W$/0.39$ A $= 3.2$ V rms. The supply voltage must then

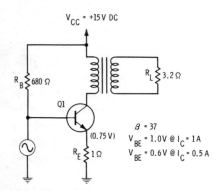

Fig. 4-30. A class-A power-amplifier stage
with transformer coupling.

be at least equal to the sum of the peak-to-peak voltage swing plus three times $V_{CE(sat)}$ plus the voltage drop across R_E. Thus the minimum value of the supply voltage is:

$$(2.8 \times 3.2) + 2 + 1 = 11.9 \text{ V}$$

(Note: Typical values of $V_{CE(sat)}$ and $I_E R_E$ have been assumed for the purpose of calculating the supply voltage.) Adding a safety margin of 25 percent, make $V_{CC} = 11.9 + 3 \cong 15$ V dc. The ac load impedance in the collector will be $R = E/I = 3.2$V$/0.39$ A $= 8.2$ ohms. This allows us to specify the transformer. The impedance ratio is 8.2 to 3.2, and the turns ratio is $\sqrt{8.2/3.2} = \sqrt{2.56} = 1.6$.

All that remains is the selection of R_E and R_B. The voltage drop across R_E should be 0.5 to 1 volt at $I_{C(Q)}$, so its value should be between 0.5 V$/0.75$ A $= 0.66$ ohm and 1 V$/0.75$ A $= 1.33$ ohms. A one-ohm resistor is a standard value in the center of this range. It must dissipate $0.75^2 \times 1 = 0.56$ watt, so a 1-watt unit should be used. Resistor R_B should supply an I_B of $I_{C(Q)}/\beta = 0.75/37 = 0.02$ A. The effective voltage across R_B is

$V_{CC} - V_{BE} - V_{RE} = 15 - 0.8 - 0.75 = 13.45$ V, so R_B is $13.45/0.02 = 672$ ohms. A 680-ohm resistor (standard value) should be used here.

Some additional power can be supplied to the load if R_E is bypassed with a capacitor so that no signal appears across it. The value of the bypass capacitor should be such that its X_C is about 0.05 R_E at the lowest frequency to be amplified. (In fact, any bypass capacitor should have an $X_C < 0.05$ R, where R is the equivalent resistance of the parallel resistors connected to the capacitor terminal.) If we use 100 Hz as the lowest frequency, X_C must be 0.05 ohm, and $C = 1/2\pi f X_C = 1/(6.28 \times 100 \times 0.05) = 32,000$ μF, a very large value. In this circuit, it would be advisable to redesign for more power instead of bypassing R_E.

A much more efficient circuit is the class-B circuit shown in Fig. 4-31. In this circuit, since each transistor is off during one half of the signal swing, the transistor dissipation is greatly reduced, and efficiency is in the area of 75 percent. Each of the transistors used in the class-A circuit can provide twice the output power in the class-B circuit for a total circuit power of four times that of Fig. 4-30.

The transistors should be selected so that they can dissipate one-half the total load power plus 25-30 percent for circuit losses. The impedance of one-half of the output-transformer primary is one-fourth of the total primary impedance. (Remember that $\sqrt{Z_P/Z_S} = N_P/N_S$, or $Z_P/Z_S = (N_P/N_S)^2$, so if N_P is divided by two, Z_P is divided by four.) Once the collector-to-

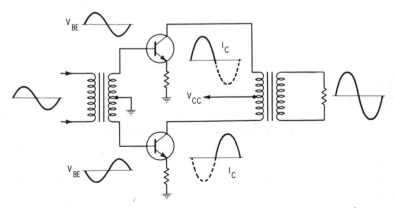

Fig. 4-31. A class-B amplifier circuit with center-tapped driver and output transformers.

V_{CC} impedance is determined, in the same way it was for a class-A stage, the turns ratio is the square root of 4 Z_{pri}/Z_{sec}, where Z_{pri} is the impedance of one-half of the primary winding.

The circuit of Fig. 4-31 has a disadvantage. Since each transistor requires at least 0.7 volt (nominal for silicon transistors) from base to emitter before conduction begins, a portion of the waveform is not reproduced. The result is crossover distortion, since a discontinuity of the signal occurs when the signal crosses over zero volts. This distortion may be eliminated by biasing the transistors by some amount so that one does not turn off before the other turns on. This is illustrated in Fig. 4-32. Operation in this manner is defined as class-AB operation. It is the usual mode of operation for audio power amplifiers.

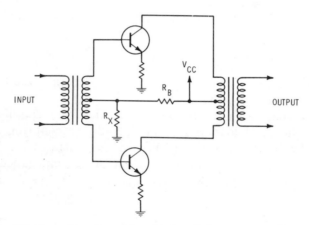

Fig. 4-32. Bias resistors R_B and R_X added to eliminate crossover distortion.

The introduction in recent years of complementary transistors (npn's and pnp's of similar electrical characteristics) has made the use of transformers in power amplifiers unnecessary. An example of a complementary-symmetry class-AB power amplifier is shown in Fig. 4-33. In this circuit, the npn transistor (Q3) conducts during the positive half cycle, and the pnp transistor (Q2) conducts during the negative half cycle of the output waveform. Resistor R_f provides current feedback to Q1 to stabilize the output point at zero volts. Diodes X1 and X2 provide a voltage drop of the proper magnitude to keep both Q2 and Q3 forward biased (to eliminate crossover distortion),

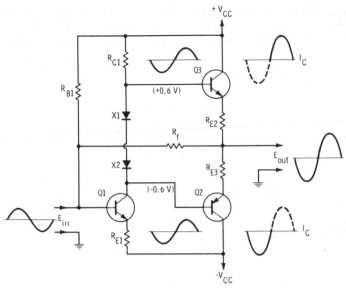

Fig. 4-33. A complementary-symmetry class-AB amplifier.

while maintaining a low impedance to both transistors for the signal at the collector of Q1.

Each transistor must dissipate one-half of the power supplied to the load. Resistors R_{E2} and R_{E3} are usually less than one ohm and are used to prevent thermal runaway, an effect that occurs if the output load impedance is reduced below its normal value, causing the transistors to overheat and destroy themselves.

Transistor Q1 is called the driver transistor in this circuit. It must supply the base current to both Q2 and Q3 through the circuit consisting of R_{E1}, Q1, X1, X2, and R_{C1}. The Q1 circuit is a class-A circuit designed so that its quiescent collector voltage is approximately 0.6 volt less than the voltage at the junction of R_{E2} and R_{E3}. A positive input signal to the base of Q1 causes it to conduct less, supplying base current to Q3 through R_{C1}. A negative input signal causes Q1 to conduct more, supplying base current to Q2 through R_{E1} and Q1.

This circuit is the simplest of all power-amplifier circuits to design and implement. For that reason, it is fast becoming the most popular circuit configuration.

The class-C amplifier circuit is used primarily in radio-frequency (rf) applications. It is biased so that it conducts for less than one-half of the signal cycle and depends on the stored energy in an inductor-capacitor (LC) circuit for restoration of the signal waveform. It is a very efficient circuit, since it can cause large amounts of power to be developed in the load while dissipating little power within itself. A class-C rf amplifier is shown in Fig. 4-34. The V_{BB} supply is used to hold the transistor off for most of the input cycle. The effects of L2 and C2 at resonance are responsible for the restoration of the output waveform.

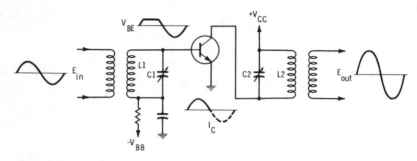

Fig. 4-34. A class-C rf amplifier.

SUMMARY

Multistage analog amplifiers are more than just a collection of single-stage circuits coupled together. They require design and analysis as systems rather than as simple units. Feedback, judiciously applied, can measurably improve the performance of a multistage circuit. Power circuits are used to drive eventual loads where small signals are inadequate.

The foundation of knowledge that has now been laid through the chapters on system design, semiconductor theory, single-stage design, and multistage circuits will be used in the following chapters as the basis for all special circuitry. If you are knowledgeable in selecting an appropriate device, biasing it, and analyzing the effect of its environment upon it, you are ready to proceed.

CHAPTER 5

Designing Signal Sources

A great many electronic projects require more than just the amplifier circuits that have been discussed thus far. One of the largest circuit categories needed is that of signal sources. Signal sources are used for generating test signals (both analog and digital), for simple things like code-practice oscillators, and for initiating and timing complex digital operations.

SINE-WAVE OSCILLATORS

The sine-wave oscillator comes in many forms, depending on the output characteristics desired. For signals in the audio-frequency range (and even up to 100 kHz or so), the simple resistor-capacitor (RC) phase-shift oscillator is usually an adequate source and is not too difficult to design. The basic phase-shift oscillator circuit is shown in Fig. 5-1. The circuit uses three RC networks to produce the required 180° phase shift from output to input.

This oscillator (as well as all oscillator circuits) makes use of positive, or regenerative, feedback. This means that a portion of the output signal is fed back "in phase" with the input signal to reinforce, or add to, that input signal. If the gain of the stage is enough to overcome the losses in the feedback network, oscillation results. The frequency of oscillation in

the circuit is determined by the values of R and C (with
$R = \beta R_E \| R_B$). At one frequency, called the frequency of oscillation or resonant frequency, the phase shift through the feedback network will be exactly equal to the 180° phase shift seen
from the base to the collector of the transistor.

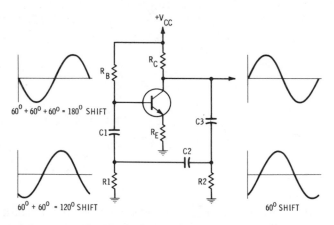

Fig. 5-1. The basic phase-shift oscillator.

How do you design a phase-shift oscillator to operate at the
amplitude and frequency you want? The step-by-step method
following the general circuit of Fig. 5-2 will illustrate the
procedure.

Step 1—Specify the output requirements and the power supply voltage. Let us assume for this example that the output must be 28 V p-p (10 V rms) at a frequency of 1000
Hz across the 500-ohms R_{E2}. The supply voltage should
then be about 1½ times this, or 42 V.

Step 2—Specify $R_{C1} \cong 0.2\ R_L$. To do this, Q2 must be biased
first. Resistor R_{E2} should drop about 21 V ($V_{CC}/2$), so the
I_C of Q2 must be approximately 42 mA. If beta equals 100,
$I_B = 0.42$ mA, and $R_{B2} = 20.4$ V/0.42 mA = 48.5K. The
nearest standard value is 50K. The value of R_L is then
$(100 \times 500)\|50{,}000 = 25{,}000$ ohms, and $R_{C1} = 0.2 \times$
$25{,}000 = 5000$ ohms.

Step 3—Calculate $R_{L(ac)}$ and $R_{E1} = R_{L(ac)}/40$. The value of
$R_{L(ac)}$ is $R_C\|R_L = (5000 \times 25{,}000)/(5000 + 25{,}000) \cong 4200$
ohms. Then $R_{E1} = 4200/40 \cong 100$ ohms. (The number 40

defines the circuit gain required to overcome losses through the network.)

Step 4—Calculate I_{C1}, I_{B1}, and R_{B1}. For normal operation, R_{C1} should drop approximately $V_{CC}/2$, so $I_{C1} = V_{CC}/2R_{C1} = 42\ V/10,000$ ohms $= 4.2$ mA. Assuming beta equals 100, $I_{B1} = 0.042$ mA. Then $R_{B1} = (V_{CC} - V_{BE1} - V_{RE1})/I_{B1} = (42\ V - 0.6\ V - 0.42\ V)/0.042$ mA $= 976K$. The nearest standard value is one megohm, and this value should work.

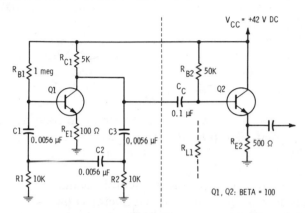

Fig. 5-2. A phase-shift oscillator loaded by an emitter follower.

Step 5—Calculate the value of R in the circuit: $R = R_{B1} || \beta R_{E1} = 1$ meg $|| (100 \times 100) \cong 10K$.

Step 6—Calculate the value of C1, C2, and C3 using the following formula:

$$C = \frac{1}{2\pi f \sqrt{6R^2 + 4RR_{C1}}} \qquad \text{(Eq. 5-1)}$$

where,

C is the capacitance in farads,
2π is a constant,
f is the desired frequency of oscillation in hertz,
R is the resistance in ohms, of one resistor (as calculated in step 5) in the phase-shift network,
R_{C1} is the resistance, in ohms, of the collector resistor.

For our circuit, $C \cong 0.0056\ \mu F$.

Step 7—Breadboard the circuit and trim the waveform purity by adjusting the value of R_{E1}. The exact frequency of oscillation may be trimmed by adjusting either "R" resistor.

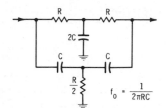

Fig. 5-3. The twin-T, or parallel-T, network.

$$f_o = \frac{1}{2\pi RC}$$

The design procedure just described will insure that the circuit will perform close to the desired characteristics. Remember that proper device selection of Q1 and Q2 is required. In this circuit, Q2 dissipates 21 V × 42 mA = 0.88 watt, so the chosen transistor should be able to dissipate at least 1.7 watts. Breakdown voltages should also be checked, since $V_{CC} = 42$ volts.

The phase-shift network from collector to base in the circuit of Fig. 5-2 may be replaced with a "twin-T" network if desired. This network and the formula for the frequency of oscillation are shown in Fig. 5-3.

While the RC phase-shift or twin-T oscillators work fine at relatively low frequencies, LC (inductor-capacitor) or crystal-controlled oscillators are normally required at radio frequencies. The LC oscillator comes in many circuit configurations, each of which is named either after the man credited with its development or for the circuit configuration.

Two of the more popular LC oscillators, the Colpitts oscillator and the tuned-collector oscillator, are shown in Figs. 5-4

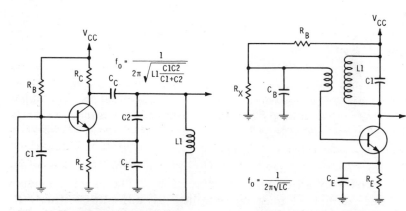

Fig. 5-4. The Colpitts oscillator.   Fig. 5-5. The tuned-collector oscillator.

and 5-5, respectively. The output from each of these oscillators is approximately equal to 0.7 times the circuit input power ($I_C \times V_{CE}$). In the Colpitts circuit, C2 is usually about three times C1. The other capacitors should have a very low X_C (<100 ohms) at the operating frequency. The dc operation and biasing of the stage are done in standard class-A fashion. The Colpitts oscillator is usually tuned by varying L1 or C1.

The tuned-collector circuit of Fig. 5-5 is biased so that $I_{C(Q)}$ is one-half the selected $I_{C(max)}$ for the circuit. Either L1 or C1 may be varied to tune the oscillating frequency. This circuit uses a pickup coil to obtain the feedback signal.

A crystal-controlled Colpitts oscillator is illustrated in Fig. 5-6. The frequency of oscillation is controlled by the crystal. The crystal replaces the inductor in the standard Colpitts circuit.

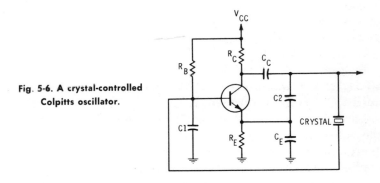

Fig. 5-6. A crystal-controlled Colpitts oscillator.

MULTIVIBRATORS

Another circuit configuration used as a signal source is the multivibrator. Multivibrators may be designed to "free-run," or oscillate, at a specific frequency, or they may be designed to put out a pulse of variable width in response to a short input pulse. A free-running multivibrator is called an astable multivibrator (since it is not stable in either state), and the circuit that puts out a single pulse in response to an input stimulus is called a monostable (or "one-shot") multivibrator. Monostable multivibrators are discussed in the chapter on digital and switching circuits.

The general circuit configuration for an astable multivibrator is shown in Fig. 5-7. An astable multivibrator uses two class-A stages with a large amount of positive feedback (through C1 and C2). Circuit operation is as follows: Assume that, at the moment power is applied to the circuit, Q1 is on (conducting) and Q2 is off (nonconducting). Transistor Q1 will remain on, due to current through C2 and R_{C2}, until C2 is charged to a value high enough to reduce the base current of Q1 below that required to keep the transistor saturated. As the voltage at the collector of Q1 begins to rise, Q2 begins to turn on. This causes C2 to discharge through R_{B1}, turning Q1

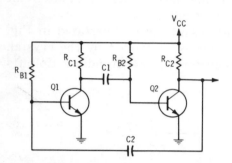

Fig. 5-7. The general circuit configuration for an astable multivibrator.

off faster and Q2 on faster. This regenerative action continues until Q1 is fully off and Q2 is fully on. Transistor Q2 will remain fully on until capacitor C1 charges (through R_{C1}). Then the collector voltage of Q2 begins to rise and C2 begins to charge. This regenerative cycle continues as long as power is applied, and the net result is a rectangular waveshape whose frequency is determined by C1 and C2 and the resistances in the circuit.

The design of an astable multivibrator is quite simple. The circuit is useful for audio testing, digital timing, power inverters, and general signal-source applications where a special output waveform is not required. First, the supply voltage is selected. In most cases, it need not be more than two or three volts greater than the peak-to-peak output voltage required (since the output swings from approximately $V_{CE(sat)}$ to almost V_{CC}). The transistors are then selected to handle the voltages and currents required. The only remaining parameters left to find are the frequency-determining component values.

The general circuit of Fig. 5-7 has some drawbacks. The most notable of these is that the rising and falling edges are not steep and the corners of the waveform tend to be rounded.

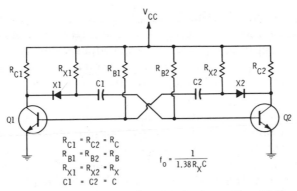

Fig. 5-8. An improved circuit configuration for the astable multivibrator.

This drawback is eliminated with the addition of diodes X1 and X2 to the circuit, as shown in Fig. 5-8. When these diodes are added, C1 and C2 charge through R_{X1} and R_{X2}, instead of R_{C1} and R_{C2}. This eliminates the rounding of the edges caused by the charging of the capacitors. Also shown in Fig. 5-8 is the formula for the frequency of oscillation of the circuit.

An actual example should best illustrate the design procedure. Suppose 10 V p-p at 1000 Hz is required, and the load resistance to be fed is 10,000 ohms. Supply voltage V_{CC} can be 12 V or greater ($V_{p-p} + V_{CE(sat)} + R_C \times I_{CBO}$ + margin). Let us assume it to be 12 V. If $R_L = 10K$, make $R_{C1} = R_{C2} = R_C = 0.2 R_L = 2000$ ohms. To bias the stages, I_C should cause a 6-V drop across R_C, so it should be 6 V/2000 ohms = 3 mA. If $\beta = 100$, $I_B = 0.03$ mA, and $R_{B1} = R_{B2} = R_B$ should be (12V − 0.6 V)/0.03 mA = 380K. Choose 390 K ohms, a standard value, for R_{B1} and R_{B2}. The frequency of oscillation is to be 1000 Hz; $R_X \times C = 1/1.38\ f_o = 0.000725$ (from the formula $f_o = 1/1.38\ R_X C$). The value for R_X is usually chosen first and may be anywhere from one to ten times R_C. The higher the value of R_X, the smaller C can be, so for this example choose $R_X \cong 10R_C = 22K$ (the nearest standard value). The value of C is then C = 0.000725/22,000 farads. Converting to microfarads, C = 0.725/22 $\cong$ 0.033 μF. This completes the design.

SAWTOOTH GENERATORS

Sawtooth (or ramp) waveforms usually require complex circuitry for their generation when bipolar transistors are used. The advent of the UJT, PUT, and FET, however, has greatly simplified the design of linear sawtooth generators. Since the circuit configurations for timers using the UJT and PUT are, in most cases, identical to the circuits used for sawtooth waveform generation, both are covered in this section, along with some pulse-generator circuits.

The basic UJT relaxation oscillator shown in Fig. 5-9 is a sawtooth generator if the output signal is taken from the emitter terminal; a pulse circuit if the output signal is taken from the base-1 terminal; and a timer if R_E is made small enough to keep the device on, once C_E has charged to a high enough value to turn the UJT on.

As you should recall from the discussion of UJT parameters in Chapter 2, the UJT conducts little current until the voltage at the emitter rises above ηV_{bb}. When the emitter voltage rises above that threshold, current is limited only by R_{B1} and R_{B2}

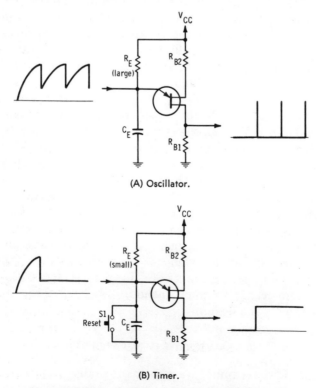

(A) Oscillator.

(B) Timer.

Fig. 5-9. The basic UJT relaxation-oscillator or timer circuit.

until the emitter current is reduced below a certain current, the valley current (I_V). Resistor R_E determines the charge rate of C_E and therefore the frequency or time period $(1/f)$ of the circuit. In circuits such as the one in Fig. 5-9A, R_E is chosen so that current through it is not enough to keep the UJT turned on. Enough current passes through R_E to charge C_E, and then C_E supplies the current to turn the UJT on. In circuits such as the one in Fig. 5-9B, R_E is chosen small enough so that current through it is enough to keep the UJT on until the circuit is reset (by S1 in Fig. 5-9B).

The design of an oscillator or timer circuit is straightforward. Resistor R_{B1} is chosen to be $0.7R_{bb}/\eta V_{CC}$ and will usually be between 20 and 100 ohms. Resistor R_{B2} is mostly for temperature compensation (so that the oscillator frequency does not vary greatly) and may be chosen to be approximately ten times R_{B1}. The emitter voltage at which the UJT will turn on (V_P) is approximately ηV_{CC} if R_{B1} is chosen as specified above.

The value of R_E is chosen to be smaller than the supply voltage minus the peak-point voltage all divided by the peak current $[R_E < (V_{CC} - \eta V_{CC})/I_P]$ and larger than the supply voltage minus the valley voltage all divided by the valley current $[R_E > (V_{CC} - V_V)/I_V]$. In practice, since most circuits must be "fine tuned" for the exact frequency desired, R_E is usually made up of two resistors, R_{E1} and R_{E2}, as in Fig. 5-10. Their values are chosen according to the formulas shown to the left of the resistors. Choosing R_{E1} and R_{E2} this way insures that the UJT will never be saturated and allows precision adjustment of the frequency.

The only remaining component value is C_E. This capacitance is chosen with R_{E2} set to the midrange value so that the tuning range of the circuit will be adequate. Capacitor C_E will charge to $0.632\ V_{CC}$ in one time constant ($R \times C$), while the circuit will turn on when $V_{CE} = V_P = \eta V_{CC}$. The frequency of oscillation is $f_o \cong 1/R_E C_E$, so $C_E = 1/R_E f_o$. For the circuit of Fig. 5-10, $C_E = 1/40,000 \times 1100 = 1/44,000,000 = 0.022\ \mu F$. The range of R_{E2} should be large enough to set the exact frequency.

To use the circuit of Fig. 5-10 as a timer, simply make R_{E1} variable and eliminate R_{E2}. Calculate $C_E = Time/R_{E1}$ with R_{E1} set to the midrange value. Capacitor C_E will begin to charge when power is applied, and the UJT will be held on (after turn on) by current through R_{E1} until it is reset by discharging C_E.

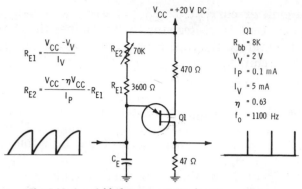

Fig. 5-10. A variable-frequency UJT relaxation oscillator.

To design a timer or oscillator with the PUT (see Fig. 5-11), set the voltage at the gate equal to $0.632\ V_{CC} - V_D$. The circuit will fire when the anode voltage reaches $0.632\ V_{CC}$, which occurs after one time constant ($R_A \times C_A$). The frequency of oscillation is $f_o = 1/(R_A \times C_A)$ for an oscillator, and the period is $R_A C_A$ for a timer. The design criteria for R_A are the same for a PUT as the criteria for R_E are for a UJT. Remember to use the values of I_P and I_V that are specified for the chosen parallel resistance of R1 and R2, since these values are programmable. It is wise to choose one of the equivalent resistance values specified on the device data sheet. For example, if you use I_P and I_V at $R_G = 10K$, make $R1 \| R2 \cong 10K$. The general equations for R1 and R2 are: $R1 \cong 1.5\ R_G$ and $R2 \cong 2.6 R_G$, where $R_G = R1 \| R2 =$ value specified on the data sheet. For the circuit of Fig. 5-11, $R1 = 15K$ and $R2 = 27K$.

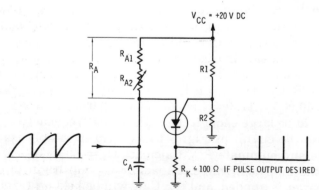

Fig. 5-11. The PUT relaxation oscillator or timer.

Then V_G is 12.85 V (approximately 0.632×20 V $- 0.5$ V), and $R_G \cong 9.65$K.

The sawtooth generators discussed so far have one major drawback—the output waveshape is exponential, rather than linear. This problem may be solved by replacing the charging resistor (R_E or R_A) with a constant-current source. This will result in a linear voltage rise across the timing capacitor (C_E or C_A). There are two methods for implementing this constant-current source, as illustrated in Fig. 5-12. The current

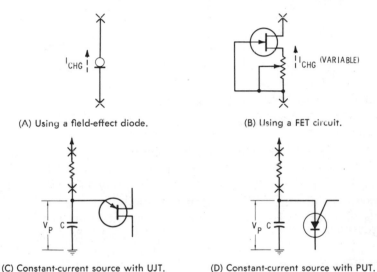

(A) Using a field-effect diode.

(B) Using a FET circuit.

(C) Constant-current source with UJT.

(D) Constant-current source with PUT.

Fig. 5-12. Constant-current sources in UJT and PUT circuits.

sources of Figs. 5-12A and 5-12B can be used in either Fig. 5-12C or 5-12D. In Figs. 5-12C and 5-12D, the X's denote the points of insertion. The field-effect diode shown in Fig. 5-12A is expensive and provides no control over the charging current (and therefore the period or frequency of oscillation). The FET circuit of Fig. 5-12B overcomes both of these disadvantages. The variable resistor in the source lead of the circuit allows V_{GS} to be varied, changing the amount of current through the device. The current may be varied over the range from approximately I_{DSS} to almost zero. For a junction FET, R_S may normally be chosen as one megohm. The value of C for either circuit configuration may be calculated by using the following formulas:

$$f_o = \frac{I_{CHG}}{C \times V_P} \quad \text{and} \quad T = \frac{C \times V_P}{I_{CHG}}$$

where,
f_o is the frequency of oscillation,
T is the period,
I_{CHG} is the charging current,
C is the capacitance in farads,
V_P is the peak-point voltage.

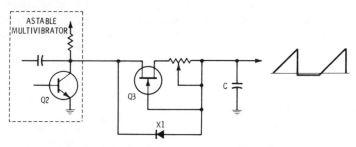

Fig. 5-13. A sawtooth generator using an astable multivibrator.

Two other interesting circuits that may be used to generate linear sawtooth waveforms are shown in Figs. 5-13 and 5-14. The astable multivibrator of Fig. 5-13 may be replaced by a "bistable" circuit (discussed in the chapter on digital circuits) if a sawtooth is required at specific time intervals (rather than free-running or unsynchronized). In Fig. 5-13, field-effect transistor Q3 provides the charge path for C at a rate of volts per second = I/C, while diode X1 provides the discharge path for C when Q2 conducts. In Fig. 5-14, capacitor C charges through Q1 until the voltage reaches the breakover voltage of X1. Current through X1 discharges C, and the cycle starts over.

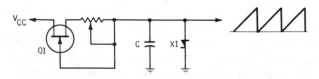

Fig. 5-14. A sawtooth generator using a four-layer diode.

PRACTICAL SIGNAL-SOURCE CIRCUITS

Now that the basic details of signal-source circuit design have been explored, let us put together some practical circuits that make use of the system design methods of Chapter 1, the basics of analog amplifiers discussed in Chapters 3 and 4, and some signal-source circuits.

One such circuit design might be the system described in Fig. 5-15, a dual-frequency audio generator that may be used, in conjunction with some other equipment designs to be discussed in later chapters, to check intermodulation distortion of amplifiers. Intermodulation distortion is the amount of undesired sum and difference frequencies at the output of an amplifier when it is being fed by a source of two frequencies.

INPUT - CLOSURE OF THE POWER SWITCH

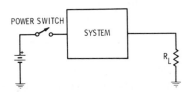

OUTPUT - A COMBINATION OF THE TWO SIGNALS, 40 Hz AND 6000 Hz, OF EQUAL AMPLITUDE (WHICH IS VARIABLE FROM ZERO TO A MINIMUM OF 3 VOLTS RMS INTO A LOAD OF 1000 Ω OR GREATER).

Fig. 5-15. A system with input and output characteristics defined.

The system description of Fig. 5-15 leads to the block diagram of Fig. 5-16, where the blocks have already been converted to circuit functions and an analysis made to determine that the design should work. Once the analysis is complete, circuit design can begin. The schematic of our system is shown in Fig. 5-17. The summing amplifier in this system schematic was chosen to be two transistors (Q3 and Q4) that use a common R_C. In this way signals from one oscillator are not fed back to the other. In the actual circuit design, it is best to work from output to input, so that each stage may be matched to the other. This is the procedure that will be followed.

The output of our system must be able to supply 8.4 V p-p to a load of 1000 ohms or greater. Since the output voltage of an emitter follower varies only slightly with changes in load resistance, R_{E5} can be specified at any value below about 1000 ohms consistent with maintaining a reasonable stage input impedance. A good rule of thumb is to select the emitter-follower resistor approximately equal to one-half the load resistance being driven. For our circuit, make $R_{E5} = 470$ ohms. Capacitor C10 should have $X_C < 1000/10 = 100$ ohms at the lowest frequency, so its value is selected as $C \geqq 1/(6.28)(40)$ $(100) = 40\ \mu F$. Use 47 μF, the next largest standard value.

Transistor Q5 must now be biased. The emitter must swing ± 4.2 V peak from the quiescent point, so select I_C to provide a drop across R_{E5} of from 4.2 V minimum to 9 V maximum $(V_{CC}/2)$. An adequate choice is 7 volts, which requires an I_C of approximately 15 mA. Then I_B is 0.15 mA. If V_{BE} is 0.7 V, $R_{B5} = (18\ V - 0.7\ V - 7\ V)/0.15\ mA \cong 68K$. The input impedance of the stage is $R_{B5}||\beta R_E||\beta R_L = 68K||47K||100K \cong 22K$. This input impedance requires X_{C9} to be less than (or equal to) $0.1 \times 22,000 = 2200$ ohms at 40 Hz. For this condition, $C_9 \geqq 1/6.28(40)(2200) = 1.8\ \mu F$. The R_L for the Q3-Q4 stage is about 22K.

Following the rule of thumb presented in Chapter 4, make R_{C3} equal to 0.2 times the R_{in} of Q5, or 4400 ohms. A 4700-ohm resistor should suffice. About 9 V p-p is needed from the Q3-Q4 stage, and about 10 V p-p is available from the Q1 and Q2 stages; thus, the gain of the Q3-Q4 stage can be made equal to one. The $R_{L(ac)}$ in the collector circuit of the Q3 portion of the stage is made up of three components—R_{C3}, R_{in} of the Q5 stage, and R_O of the Q4 stage. Similarly, the $R_{L(ac)}$ in the Q4 portion

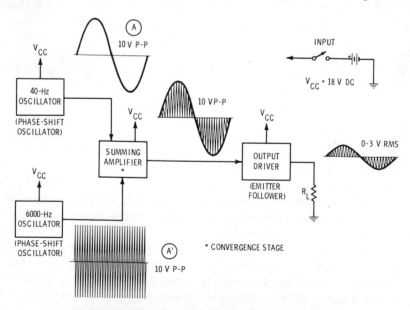

Fig. 5-16. The block-diagram creation, conversion, and analysis.

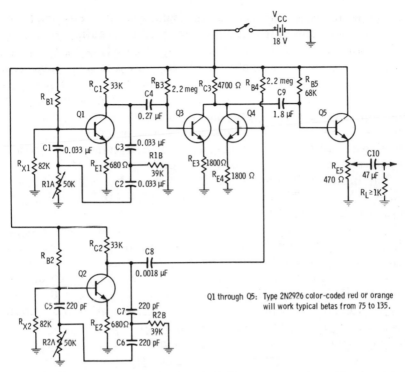

Fig. 5-17. Circuit configuration of dual-frequency generator with component values shown.

of the stage is made up of $R_{C3}||R_{in}$ of the Q5 stage$||R_O$ of Q3. To approximate the value of R_O, assume a 1 mA change in the collector current of Q3 (or Q4, since we are using the same device in both places, and they are connected to the same R_C). The 1-mA change in I_C will result in a 4.7-volt change in the drop across R_{C3} (and therefore, the V_{CE} of the transistor). Therefore $R_O = \Delta V_{CE}/\Delta I_C = 4.7$ V/1 mA = 4.7K. Then $R_{L(ac)}$ is equal to 4.7K$||$22K$||$4.7K $\cong$ 2100 ohms. For the voltage gain of Q3 or Q4 to be at least one, make $R_{E3} = R_{E4}$ less than or equal to 2100 ohms. Using 1800 ohms insures that adequate gain will be available.

Since R_{E3} and R_{E4} are large in relation to R_{C3}, the quiescent collector voltage at the bottom of R_{C3} should be set higher than $V_{CC}/2$. Since I_C should never go to zero, set I_C so that the drop across R_{C3} is 5 volts (one-half the p-p voltage) plus one volt (for good measure), or 6 volts. Current I_C is made up of two equal components—I_{CQ3} and I_{CQ4}—so the individual collector currents will be set to one-half the value required to obtain a 6 V drop across R_{C3}. For 6 V across R_{C3}, $I_{C(total)} = 6$ V/4700 ohms = 1.28 mA. The collector currents for Q3 and Q4 are then each 0.64 mA. The base current, I_B, will be 0.0064 mA (6.4 μA), so $R_{B3} = R_{4B} = [18$ V $- 0.7$ V $- (0.64$ mA $\times 1800$ ohms)]/6.4 μA = 2.5 megohms. Using 2.2-megohm standard-value resistors will result in more quiescent collector current, so there is no danger that the I_C of Q3 or Q4 will become zero (which would result in distortion of the output signals).

The input impedance to the Q3-Q4 stage is 2.2 meg$||$180K $\cong$ 165K. Then C4 should be $\geq 1/6.28(40)(0.1)(165K) \cong 0.27$ μF, and C8 should be $\geq 1/6.28$ (6000)(0.1)(165K ohms) = 0.0018 μF. With the input impedance of Q3 (or Q4) at 165K, R_{C1} (or R_{C2}) should be about (0.2)(165K) = 33K. The $R_{L(ac)}$ of Q1 (and Q2) = 33K$||$165K $\cong$ 27.5K. For a phase-shift oscillator, A_V should be about 40, so $R_{E1} = R_{E2} \cong 680$ ohms. The collector current of Q1 (and Q2) should cause a 9-V drop across R_{C1} (and R_{C2}). Therefore I_C should be 9 V/33K = 0.27 mA, and I_B should then be 2.7 μA (0.0027 mA). Then $R_{B1} = R_{B2}$ equals [18 V $-$ 0.7 V $- (0.27$ mA $\times 680$ ohms)]/2.7 μA $\cong$ 6.8 megohms.

The value 6.8 megohms for R_{B1} and R_{B2} is quite high for a bipolar transistor circuit, and noise generated within the resistor may be amplified by the transistor, resulting in undesired noise in the output signal. In this instance, it would be wise to add resistors R_{X1} and R_{X2} to the Q1 and Q2 stages. These resistors, in addition to reducing circuit noise, will improve the stability of the stages (as described in Chapter 3).

Let $R_{X1} = R_{X2}$ carry $4 \times I_{B1} = 4 \times I_{B2}$. With (0.27 mA $\times$ 680 ohms) + 0.7 V $\cong$ 0.9 V dropped across $R_{X1} = R_{X2}$ at a current of 4×2.7 μA = 10.8μA, $R_{X1} = R_{X2} \cong$ 82K. The total current through R_{B1} or R_{B2} is 10.8 + 2.7 = 13.5 μA, and the voltage across the resistor is 18 $-$ 0.9 = 17.1 V. Therefore $R_{B1} = R_{B2} =$ 17.1 V/13.5 μA $\cong$ 1.2 megohms, a much better value for this type of circuit. Now R1 = R2 = R_{in} of the Q1 and Q2 stages is 1.2 meg$||$82K$||$(100)(680) $\cong$ 36K. Using a 50K potentiometer for R1A = R2A allows adjustment to the exact frequencies desired. Resistors R1B and R2B may then be 39K, a standard value.

The only remaining calculations are those for the nominal values of C1, C2, C3, C5, C6, and C7. These values are computed by substituting the appropriate values into Equation 5-1. In this case, R is 36K (as just calculated), and the value of R_C is 33K for both Q1 and Q2. For the Q1 stage, f is 40 Hz, so:

$$C1 = C2 = C3 = \frac{1}{6.28(40)\sqrt{6(36K)^2 + 4(36K)(33K)}}$$
$$\cong 0.033 \ \mu F$$

For the Q2 stage, f is 6000 Hz, so:

$$C5 = C6 = C7 = \frac{1}{6.28(6000)\sqrt{6(36K)^2 + 4(36K)(33K)}}$$
$$\cong 0.00022 \ \mu F = 220 \ pF$$

The active devices (transistors) are selected so that their maximum ratings are not exceeded and their beta values are approximately equal to 100, the value used in the design steps. Design values for all components are shown in Fig. 5-17.

A design of the type just completed requires many steps and takes much thought to complete. Looked upon as a challenge, however, it can be fun to do. It should be kept in mind that the circuit just designed may not work perfectly when power is applied to it, but it will work. Final optimization of each component when the circuit is actually constructed will probably be required if ideal performance is to be expected.

Many designs require only one or two stages to complete. An example of this is the 100-kHz crystal-controlled oscillator illustrated in Fig. 5-18. This circuit, which uses a bipolar transistor and a FET for the active elements, may be used as a calibration aid for radio receivers, so that the dial may be accurately set. If we use a 9-V transistor-radio battery for the

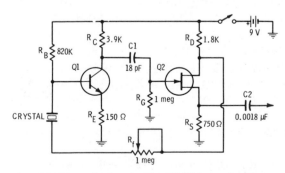

Fig. 5-18. Schematic diagram of a 100-kHz crystal calibrator.

supply voltage (to make the unit self-powered and portable), the voltage at the collector of Q1 and the drain of Q2 will be about five to six volts. Since this is a low-power circuit, almost any transistor will work. Arbitrarily select the collector current of Q1 to be 1 mA and the drain current of Q2 to be $I_{DSS}/2 = 2$ mA with $V_{GS} = -1.5$ V (I_{DSS} being equal in this example to 4 mA). Since we do not know the value of the series impedance of the crystal at its resonant frequency (100 kHz), we do not know the minimum required open-loop A_V of the circuit. However, if Q1 has a reasonable input impedance, we could assume that an overall gain of 50 would allow an $A_f \geqq 1$, the necessary condition for oscillation. The required gain will probably be much less than 50, so R_f is included to set the exact frequency and waveshapes desired. The value of R_f is found experimentally on the bench by using a high-value potentiometer, say one megohm, for a starting value. Adjust the potentiometer for the desired results.

If $A_{V(total)} = 50$, as a trial configuration, let each stage have an A_V of approximately 7. Since Q2 requires a drop of 1.5 V across R_S at 2 mA I_D for proper bias, $R_S = 1.5$ V$/2$ mA $= 750$ ohms. For a stage $A_V = 7$, $R_D = 7$ $R_S = 5250$ ohms (ignoring the loading effect of R_f and the crystal). If $R_D = 5250$ ohms, however, 10.5 V will be dropped across it at $I_D = 2$ mA, an impossible situation. If the voltage at the Q2 drain terminal is to be five to six volts, only three to four volts may be dropped across R_D, so its value is restricted to the range of $R_D = 3$ V$/2$ mA $= 1500$ ohms to 4 V$/2$ mA $= 2000$ ohms. Use a standard-value 1800-ohm resistor. The A_V of the Q2 stage (assuming $y_{fs} = 5000$ μmhos) is then approximately 2. Let $R_G = 1$ megohm, a value almost universally applicable to JFET circuits.

For a total A_V of 50, the A_V of the Q1 stage must be $50/2 = 25$. If the collector voltage of Q1 is to be five to six volts, R_C may be between (9 V $- 5$V)$/1$ mA $= 4000$ ohms and (9 V $- 6$ V)$/1$ mA $= 3000$ ohms. Use a 3900-ohm resistor. If $A_V = 25$, $R_E = 3900/25 = 156$ ohms. The standard value is 150 ohms. If beta $= 100$, $R_{in} = 15,000$ ohms, a reasonably high value. Then $R_B = (V_{CC} - V_{BE} - V_{RE})/I_B = (9$ V $- 0.7$ V $- 0.15$ V$)/10$ μA $= 8.15$ V$/10$ μA $= 0.815$ megohm. A standard-value 820K resistor will probably work well.

The remaining components are C1 and C2. Since $R_G = 1$ megohm, X_{C1} should be less than 0.1 megohm at 100 kHz. Therefore,

C1 $\geqq 1/(2\pi)(0.1 \times 10^6)(100 \times 10^3) = 1/2\pi(10 \times 10^9) = 1/2\pi$ $(0.01 \times 10^{12}) = 1 \times 10^{-12}/0.0628 = 16$ picofarads   (picofarads = farads $\times 10^{-12}$). Use a standard 18-pF capacitor. Assuming C2 will feed a much lower impedance than C1, make it 100 times as large, or $18 \times 10^{-12} \times 100 = 1800 \times 10^{-12} = 0.0018 \times 10^{-6} = 0.0018$ microfarad. Resistor R_f is used to adjust the circuit to the exact frequency.

The type of design procedure presented for the circuit of Fig. 5-18 must seem like a very unscientific method after the attention to detail and calculation given to all of the previous circuit designs. It was presented in this fashion to make a point. When there are a number of unknown (or unspecifiable) parameters to be considered, make some assumptions and design a trial circuit. Once it is functioning (in some manner) and connected to its ultimate source, load, and feedback components, analyze the design problems in an attempt to specify some of the unknowns so that a more refined circuit-design approach may be applied. The more unknowns that can be eliminated, the better the circuit design will be. There is almost always enough information to allow you to make some assumptions and assign some arbitrary values as a starting point.

SUMMARY

Analog amplifiers can be converted into signal-source circuits by applying positive feedback to them. Devices designed especially for oscillator and timer circuits (such as the PUT and UJT) require only the addition of the appropriate frequency-determining components for proper operation.

Signal sources are used to generate sine-wave, square-wave, and sawtooth-wave signals for a variety of uses. Each circuit has certain advantages, and the circuit selected for a particular application should be analyzed to insure its suitability.

CHAPTER 6

Designing Signal Detectors

Once a signal has been generated, amplified, and used, it must usually be "detected" before it can be made to do useful work. Detection, as used in this chapter, refers to the identification of input signals and input signal differences so that useful information may be extracted from them. Our definition of a signal detector is, therefore, much broader than the normal definition (which is usually confined to radio work).

Perhaps the simplest example of a signal detector is the single-stage circuit of Fig. 6-1. In this circuit, lamp M1 replaces the collector resistor and indicates either the presence or absence of an input signal. When a dc level of the proper size and polarity is applied to R1, base current flows in Q1, turning it on and lighting M1. If the input signal is removed, there is no bias for Q1 and therefore not enough collector current to turn M1 on.

If we wish to detect and indicate the presence or absence of an ac input signal, it is only necessary to add the half-wave rectifier circuit consisting of X1 and X2 shown in Fig. 6-2. Diode X1 clamps the input to X2 (and therefore Q1) at approximately -0.7 V and provides a discharge path for C1 when X2 is reverse biased during the negative half cycle of the input. During the positive half cycle, X2 (and the base-emitter junction of Q1) is forward biased, causing base current (and collector current) through the transistor. Lamp M1 is turned on and will appear to be steadily on if the frequency of the input signal is above about 40 Hz.

The only real design constraints on the circuits of Figs. 6-1 and 6-2 are that the transistor be able to handle the lamp current and that R1 be chosen so that the magnitude of I_B when the input signal is applied, is such that βI_B is equal to or greater than the current required by the lamp with $V_{CC} - V_{CE(sat)}$ across it.

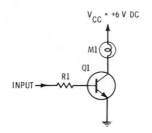

Fig. 6-1. A simple signal-detector circuit configuration.

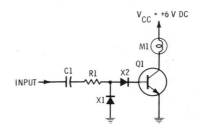

Fig. 6-2. The ac version of the simple signal detector.

THRESHOLD DETECTION

Of more practical value than the circuits just discussed is a class of signal detectors called threshold detectors. A threshold detector provides a given output when its input signal exceeds (or, in some cases, is less than) a prespecified value. A simple threshold detector, a modification of the circuit of Fig. 6-1, is shown in Fig. 6-3. Potentiometer R1 allows the turn-on point of Q1 to be adjusted to the desired value and is adjusted so that the lamp is off until the input exceeds the value necessary to provide Q1 with sufficient I_B to turn it on.

The major disadvantage of the circuit of Fig. 6-3 is that the collector current of Q1 rises gradually with the input voltage increase, rather than quickly increasing to its maximum value when the threshold is exceeded. This results in a rather constant glow in M1 unless large voltage changes are being detected. The addition of a zener diode to the circuit will alleviate this problem. Three approaches to dc threshold detection using zener diodes are shown in Fig. 6-4.

The circuits of Fig. 6-4A and 6-4B light M1 when the input exceeds the preset value, while the circuit of Fig. 6-4C lights

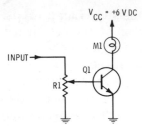

V_CC = +6 V DC

Fig. 6-3. A simple adjustable level detector circuit.

M1 when the input is less than the preset value. In the circuit of Fig. 6-4A, when the voltage across the bottom portion of R1 exceeds the breakdown voltage (V_z) of the zener diode, base current is produced, turning on Q1 and M1. While this circuit has much more of a "snap action" effect than the previously discussed circuits, the leakage current through X1 may be enough to cause a dim glow in M1, even though V_{in} is below the turn-on threshold. This problem may be eliminated, at the expense of a higher input current requirement, by adding R2 in Fig. 6-4B. The value of R2 is chosen so that any leakage current through X1 is shunted to ground. When V_{in} increases and causes X1 to go into conduction, the current is shared between R2 and Q1. Since the current through X1 is many times greater when the diode is in the breakdown region than when

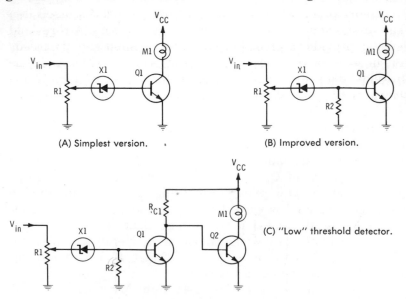

(A) Simplest version.

(B) Improved version.

(C) "Low" threshold detector.

Fig. 6-4. Three threshold detectors using zener diodes.

it is not conducting, there is enough current to turn on Q1 and M1.

The circuit of Fig. 6-4C lights M1 when the input voltage is below the prespecified threshold. When V_{in} is large enough to keep X1 and Q1 turned on, Q2 (and therefore M1) is kept off. If V_{in} goes below the value required to insure conduction through X1, Q1 turns off, allowing the collector voltage to rise and current to flow in the base-emitter junction of Q2. This causes M1 to light.

In cases where a more sensitive circuit is needed, the circuit of Fig. 6-5 may be used. We will use this circuit as a design example, since the design steps for this circuit should illustrate how to design any of the previous circuits. The circuit of Fig. 6-5 uses a JFET input stage to achieve a high input resistance. Diode X1 is placed between Q1 and Q2 so that its leakage current may be shunted away from the base of Q2 without degrading the input sensitivity. Resistor R_G is the standard value for practical JFET circuits and is used for gate biasing in this sensitive FET-pnp threshold detector circuit. We wish to detect any voltage above +6 volts on a line that is nominally at 5 volts.

For the purposes of illustration, assume M1 is a 24-V, 100-mA lamp. The I_C of Q2 should therefore be equal to or greater than 100 mA, so I_B should be at least 1 mA, assuming that beta = 100. Select $I_{B(on)} = 2I_{B(min)} = 2$ mA. If the current through X1 is 0.1 mA maximum before breakdown, R1 should be chosen so that less than approximately 0.7 volt is dropped across it at 0.1 mA. Then R1 = 0.7 V/0.1 mA = 7000 ohms. Let R1 be 6800 ohms, a standard value. When X1 is conducting

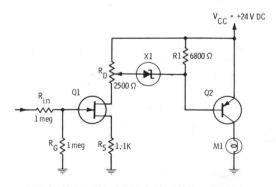

Fig. 6-5. A FET-input threshold detector.

2 mA, and Q2 requires > 1 mA I_B to turn on M1, the effect of R1 may be ignored. (The current through it will be less than 10 percent of the current through X1.) If the I_{DSS} of Q1 is 10 mA and $I_D = 5$ mA at $V_{GS} = -3$ V, we can calculate the values of R_{in} and R_S. There is considerable latitude at this point. If $R_{in} = 0$, there should be a voltage drop of 8 V across R_S when $I_D = 5$ mA, because this would make V_{GS} equal to $5 - 8 = -3$ V when the voltage being monitored has the nominal value of 5 volts. If we let $R_{in} = R_G = 1$ meg, $V_G = 2.5$ V, and R_S would only need to drop 5.5 V to keep V_{GS} at -3 V. If $R_{in} = 10$ R_G $= 10$ meg, R_S should drop about 3.5 V. Since $V_{CC} = 24$ V, any of these values will work. If we elect to have the input resistance of the circuit on the order of 1-to-2 megohms, a value of R_{in} equal to 1 megohm is a good choice. The value of R_S is therefore 5.5 V/5 mA $= 1.1$K. If we make $V_{DS} = V_{RD} = (V_{CC} - V_{RS})/2 = (24 - 5.5)/2 = 9.25$ V, R_D should drop 9.25 V at $I_D = 5$ mA and should be 9.25 V/5 mA $\cong 1900$ ohms. Use a 2500-ohm potentiometer, the next largest standard-value unit. This will still allow an adequate V_{DS} across Q1 ($\cong 6$ V) and provide adequate diode current through R_S, Q1, and R_D to turn on Q2.

To choose X1 so that the threshold can be set accurately, assume that R_D is set to midrange so that the voltage at the anode of X1 is 17.75 volts. The voltage at the base of Q2 (conducting) is approximately 23.3 volts, so zener diode X1 should have a $V_Z = 23.3 - 17.75 = 5.5$ V. A standard zener voltage is 5.6 V at plus or minus 20 percent (that is why we need an adequate range for potentiometer R_D).

We now have all of the component values. To use the circuit, however, it must first be calibrated. Set the wiper of R_D at the $+V_{CC}$ end of the potentiometer and apply $+6$ V to the V_{in} terminal. Slowly adjust R_D away from the V_{CC} end until M1 just turns on—then stop. When the input voltage is returned to the nominal value, M1 should go out. Raising V_{in} to $+6$ V should cause M1 to light again.

Since the knee of a zener diode is not perfectly square but slightly rounded, M1 will probably not turn off if V_{in} is reduced to 5.9 volts, for example. It will be necessary to reduce V_{in} enough to allow the zener to stop conducting. This effect is called *hysteresis* and is evident in almost all threshold detection circuits. Because of hysteresis, threshold detector circuits must be calibrated to turn on (or off) when the input voltage increases (or decreases) above (or below) the preset value.

Two threshold detector circuits, one using a PUT and one a triac, are shown in Fig. 6-6. These two threshold detector circuits are quite simple to design and are useful in many non-precision applications. The capacitor in Fig. 6-6B is used to prevent noise from triggering the thyristor circuit. Each circuit has its own particular advantages, disadvantages, and special applications. The PUT circuit has a variable hysteresis which is set by programming the I_P and I_V current values (the closer I_P is to I_V, the less is the hysteresis). The threshold voltage is about 0.5 V greater than the voltage at the gate. The triac circuit automatically resets itself and is used to activate ac loads.

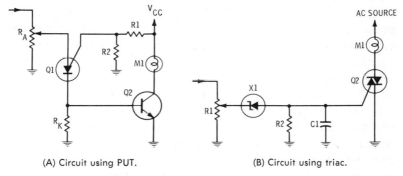

(A) Circuit using PUT.   (B) Circuit using triac.

Fig. 6-6. Two typical threshold detector circuits.

PULSE DETECTION

For many project applications it may be necessary to detect the presence or absence of a pulse (or train of pulses), rather than just a dc or ac level. One such application is the power-supply transient-monitoring circuit shown on Fig. 6-7. In this circuit (which is simply a latching threshold detector), any voltage spike or pulse exceeding the preset limit turns on the lamp. The lamp remains on until the circuit is manually reset. If we want to detect the presence or absence of pulses of any amplitude (above about one volt peak), zener diode X1 and potentiometer R1 can be removed and replaced by a capacitor. The capacitor will couple any pulses or spikes while ignoring the dc level at the input.

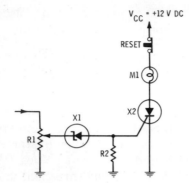

Fig. 6-7. A latching pulse detector circuit.

All of the threshold and pulse detectors discussed so far have one thing in common—they are all designed to be used with positive voltage or positive pulse inputs. For negative-polarity inputs, the bipolar circuits should use negative V_{CC} and pnp devices. Remember to change the polarity of the other semiconductors and any electrolytic capacitors when redesigning for the opposite polarity. To convert the thyristor detection circuits for both negative and positive pulse inputs, the circuit of Fig. 6-8 can be used. Diodes X1 and X2 (with capacitors C2 and C3) provide isolation between the collector and emitter of the transistor. The gain of the Q1 stage is made equal to one by making $R_C = R_E$. Positive input pulses are coupled through C3 and X2, while negative input pulses are inverted by Q1 and coupled through C2 and X1. Resistors R1 and R2 provide discharge paths for capacitors C2 and C3. Their value may be from one to ten times R_E. To use the circuit of Fig. 6-8 in the

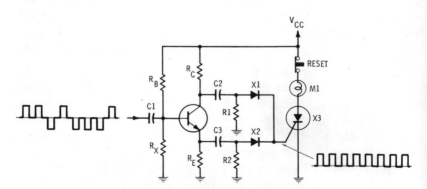

Fig. 6-8. A "bipolar" pulse detector circuit.

nonlatching mode, connect the lamp to an ac source instead of to V_{CC}. For ac loads, use a triac.

In all of the signal detector circuits shown so far, a lamp has been used as the indicating device. It may be replaced with any other type of load as long as the output stage can drive the selected load.

DEMODULATION

Demodulation is the term applied to the areas of signal detection where information, or intelligence, is extracted from an incoming signal which has been modulated, or changed in some fashion, by the addition of an information-bearing signal. The two most common forms of information-bearing signals are amplitude modulated (a-m) signals and frequency modulated (fm) signals. To extract the information at the receiving end, we use a detector circuit.

An a-m detector and the voltage waveforms present at its various points are shown in Fig. 6-9. Since the amplitude of the incoming signal is changing with the information being applied to it, if we rectify and filter the signal, all that remains are the amplitude variations—the information. Although the signals along the line connected to the cathode of X1 are actually identical, three waveforms are shown in Fig. 6-9 to illustrate the operation of C1 and C2.

Demodulating an fm signal is more complex. The input, unmodulated, is a continuous-wave (cw) signal at the carrier, or center, frequency. For our example, assume this frequency to be 10.7 MHz. When the modulating signal is applied, the carrier frequency varies above and below the center 10.7-MHz value. To extract the information from the signal, we must convert these frequency variations to amplitude variations that

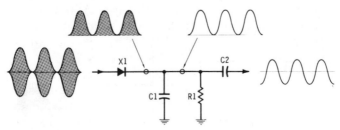

Fig. 6-9. An amplitude modulation (a-m) detector.

can be applied to an amplifier and subsequently to an output device.

One circuit for demodulating an fm signal is shown in Fig. 6-10. This circuit is known as a discriminator. At the center frequency, the voltages at the ends of coils L2 and L3 are equal. The equal currents through R1 and R2 result in equal drops across them, and $E1 - E2 = E_{out} = 0$ V. When the frequency swings to one side, the current caused by the combination of the reference voltage (through C1) and the coil voltage is different for R1 than it is for R2. The difference between E1 and E2 no longer equals zero. If the frequency swings in the opposite direction, the difference between E1 and E2 will be of the opposite polarity. The frequency variations at the input are thus converted to voltage variations at the output.

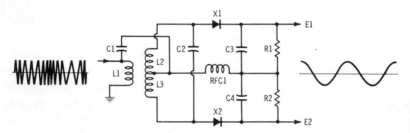

Fig. 6-10. A frequency modulation (fm) discriminator.

Another circuit used to demodulate fm signals is the ratio detector circuit of Fig. 6-11. In this circuit, the output is taken at the junction of C2 and C3. At the center frequency, the voltage across C2 equals the voltage across C3, and the sum of the voltages across C2 and C3 is the voltage across C5 and R1. On one side of the center frequency, the current through X1 (and therefore the voltage across C2) is greater than the current through X2. The total voltage across C2 and C3 remains the same (one increases and the other decreases), but the ratio of the voltages has changed. On the other side of the center frequency, the ratio changes in the opposite direction (the voltage across C3 is greater than the voltage across C2).

The values for R1 and C5 are usually chosen so that the time constant ($R \times C$) of the circuit is approximately 0.2 second or so (much longer than the period of the lowest frequency to be demodulated). Typical values are 22K and 10 μF, respectively. The remaining components are chosen so that the circuit is

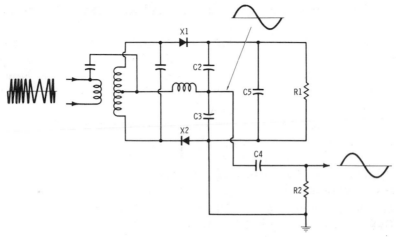

Fig. 6-11. A ratio detector circuit.

resonant at the center (or carrier) frequency. Capacitors C2 and C3 are chosen so that their impedance is low at the center frequency but reasonably high at the highest "information" signal frequency. Resistor R2 is usually the input resistance to the next stage, and C4 is chosen so that its X_C is less than or equal to 0.1R2.

CONVERTING NONELECTRICAL EVENTS TO ELECTRICAL SIGNALS

So far we have dealt only with electrical signals as inputs to our circuits. What if we want to use temperature changes or changes in the intensity of a light source as the input signal to be detected? To make these signals or events useable, we must convert them into electrical signals and interface them to our circuitry.

Converting temperature variations to electrical variations is a relatively simple matter. We use a device called a *thermistor*. The symbol for the thermistor and the simplest way to use it are shown in Fig. 6-12. The value of R1 may be chosen equal to the resistance of the thermistor at the desired midpoint operating temperature. Thermistors are available in resistances from about 2000 ohms up to one megohm (at 25°C). The higher the resistance of the thermistor, the greater the ratio of cold-to-hot resistance.

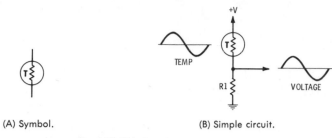

| (A) Symbol. | (B) Simple circuit. |

Fig. 6-12. The thermistor.

The thermistor can be used as the input to a threshold detector where an off/on indication or control signal is the desired output. The circuit of Fig. 6-13 illustrates one such use. When the thermistor temperature rises above the temperature that corresponds to the setting of potentiometer R1, the lamp turns on. The only thermistor parameter that is really critical is the device dissipation. It should not be exceeded. (Replacing M1 with a relay that controls an air conditioner converts this circuit into a useful project.)

Converting variations in the intensity of light to electrical signals is just as simple as the conversion of temperature variations, and there are a number of devices used to perform this conversion. The photovoltaic cell (PVC), more commonly called a *sun battery,* is one method. The light-sensitive or light-dependent resistor (LDR) is another. Finally, there are the active devices, the phototransistor and the light-activated silicon controlled rectifier (LASCR).

The photovoltaic cell is a popular light-to-electricity transducer because, unlike all other light-controlled devices, it requires no external power supply. When subjected to strong light, it actually generates a voltage that will cause current

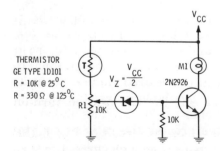

Fig. 6-13. A temperature sensing circuit.

The heart of the circuit is the combination of T1, X1, X2, potentiometer R1, and the thermistor. When the resistance of the thermistor is equal to the resistance of the potentiometer, the voltage at their common point (point A in Fig. 6-16) is zero. Should the value of the thermistor increase, due to a lower room temperature, the voltage at point A becomes negative (actually a portion of the negative half cycle of the 60-Hz voltage from T1). If the thermistor resistance decreases, the voltage at point A becomes positive.

The signal at point A is amplified by Q1 and split into two phases by the Q2 stage. The signals are then coupled to driver transistors Q3 and Q4 through C3 and C4. Diodes X3 and X4 provide discharge paths for C3 and C4.

To design this circuit, start at the output. It the heater and air conditioner each require 250 watts, the current through each will be approximately 2.1 ampere ac. Since they run off 117 V ac, the breakover voltage of the triacs should be at least 1.4×117 V ac $\cong 164$ volts and preferably higher. The RCA 40429 triac is rated at 6 A (rms) I_T and 200 V (minimum) V_{RM}. It should be adequate if it is mounted on a heat sink. The gate characteristics are: $V_{GT} = 1$ V (typical) and 2.2 V (maximum), and $I_{GT} = 20$ mA (typical) and 25 mA (maximum). If we aim for a V_{GT} of 2.0 V @ I_{GT} of 20 mA we should insure stable triggering without overstressing the device.

We should select R9 and R10 so that they draw about 0.1 I_{GT} @ V_{GT}. This keeps the transistor dissipation down while insuring that any transistor leakage is shunted to ground and cannot turn the triac on. The value of R9 = R10 should be 2 V/$(0.1 \times 20$ mA$) = 1K$, a standard value. Next, select the transistors. Since all the circuits are of relatively low power, almost any device will work if it can handle $V_{CC} = 16$ V and $I_C = 22$ mA. The 2N2926 may be used. This transistor type is color coded to show the ac beta range, and one coded red or orange (typical betas from 75 to 135) will work. A beta of 100 is assumed in the example for ease of calculations.

Since the emitter current of Q3 (and Q4) is approximately 20 mA at an emitter voltage of about 2 V, the equivalent emitter resistance is 100 ohms. This means that the stage input impedance is 100 ohms $\times 100 = 10K$. The X_C of C3 and C4 at 60 Hz should be less than $0.1 \times 10K = 1K$ for good coupling. Make C3 = C4 $\geq 1/(6.28)(60)(1000) \cong 1/380,000 = 1 \times 10^{-6}/$

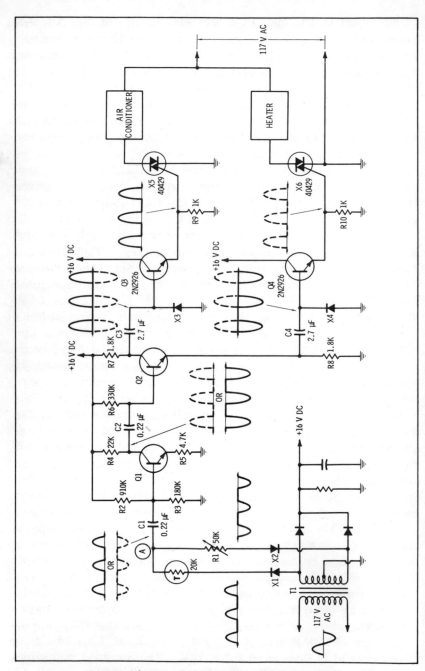

Fig. 6-16. Schematic of an automatic temperature controller.

0.38 $\cong$ 2.7 μF. The Q2 stage will have a gain of one to obtain equal signals from both collector and emitter. Make R7 = R8 $\cong$ (0.2)(10K) = 2K. (This is one-fifth of the following stage input impedance, as has been used in previous designs.) The next lowest standard value is 1800 ohms.

The drop across R7 should equal the drop across R8 and the V_{CE} of Q2. Since $V_{CC} = 16$ V dc, the drop will be about 5.35 volts for R7 and R8. The I_C of Q2 for a 5.35-volt drop across the 1800-ohm R7 should be 5.35 V/1800 ohms $\cong$ 3 mA. Then, if beta = 100, I_B will be 0.03 mA. The voltage at the base of Q2 will be approximately 6 V, so R6 should drop $16 - 6 = 10$ V at 0.03 mA. Its value is then 10 V/0.03 mA = 330K.

The Q1 stage is the convergence stage in this design. We must make the input requirements of the Q2 stage match the stimulus available from the thermistor and R1. We have a gain of about one from the input of Q2 to the triac gates, where we need 2-V peak. Adding some margin to account for circuit losses (through the capacitors and the V_{BE} drop of Q3 and Q4), let us aim for 3-V peak (6 V peak-to-peak) at the collector of Q1.

We wish to detect $\pm$5-percent changes in the temperature. With about 16-V peak at the end points, a 5-percent change represents about 0.8 V peak. For 3-V peak output, the A_V of the Q1 stage should be $3/0.8 \cong 4$. The value of R4 should be about 0.2 times R_{in} of Q2, or $(0.2)(330K||1800 \times 100) \cong 23K$; the nearest standard value is 22K. The ac load, $R_{L(ac)}$, for Q1 is 22K||116K $\cong$ 18.5K, so for a gain of 4, R5 should be 18.5K/4 = 4.6K. There is some slack in the gain calculation, so make R5 = 4.7K.

For the Q1 stage, $I_{C(max)}$ is 16 V/26.7K = 0.6 mA, so set $I_{C(Q)}$ at 0.3 mA. Then I_B is 0.003 mA. The voltage at the base is 0.3 mA $\times$ 4.7K + 0.7 V = 2.1 V. Resistor R3 should draw about 4 times I_B, or 0.012 mA, with 2.1 V across it, so R3 = 2.1 V/0.012 mA $\cong$ 180K. Resistor R2 should drop $16 - 2.1 = 13.9$ V at $0.012 + 0.003 = 0.015$ mA. Therefore R2 = 13.9 V/0.015 mA $\cong$ 910K.

We still need values for C1 and C2: C2 $\geqq$ 1/(6.28)(60)(11.6K) $\cong$ 0.22 μF. The input impedance of the Q1 stage is approximately 130K, which is slightly larger than the input impedance (116K) of the Q2 stage. The value of C1, therefore, could be slightly smaller than the value of C2, but the same standard value of 0.22 μF can be used for both. With the input impedance to the Q1 stage approximately 130K, the value of R1 and the thermistor should be between 13K and 26K. A 20K thermistor is a standard value. Choose R1 to be a 50K potentiometer and set it approximately to midrange. Diodes X1 through X4 can be low-voltage, low-current silicon units of almost any type. The design of the power supply is covered in Chapter 10.

This completes the design. The circuit probably will not work—perfectly that is. It, like most other circuits designed around "typical" device values, will need some adjustments on the bench. The biggest change that may be required, however, is the value of R5 to either increase or decrease the voltage gain of the Q1 stage. A thorough analysis shows that the basic design is sound.

SUMMARY

Designing a circuit to detect an input, or a change in the input signal, requires the proper selection of the input transducer and an accurate description of the input signal characteristics to be detected.

Note that signal detectors, like signal sources, are designed around or built from modified single- or multiple-stage analog amplifiers for the most part. Other devices such as the PUT, LDR, PVC, phototransistor, and SCR are also useful in certain applications.

If the design of a circuit is approached in a logical manner, as the system design was done, most circuits will function to some extent when first assembled, and they should work perfectly with only minor component-value adjustment.

In the next chapter, we turn to some special-purpose circuits that do not qualify for either this or the previous chapter.

CHAPTER 7

Special-Purpose Analog Circuits

The number of circuits that can be included in the category of special-purpose analog circuits is probably infinite. There are circuits in existence to perform almost any conceivable analog function, and new circuits are constantly being developed to perform more special functions. To cover all of them would be a monumental (if not impossible) task, but some of the more popular special circuit functions are covered in detail in the following sections. It should be remembered that none of the circuits are sacred—they can (and should) be modified or used as the basis for a new circuit to do the job at hand.

GATED AMPLIFIERS

A gated amplifier is a circuit designed to provide an output in response to an input only when a control signal tells it to do so. A simplified example of this is shown in Fig. 7-1, where a relay is used to connect the input signal to the amplifier in response to a dc control signal input. While this circuit does qualify as a gated amplifier, it has several disadvantages. Among these are the need for a control signal with considerable current capacity (to operate the relay coil) and the noise that is introduced in the output when the relay contacts close.

Since the contacts of a relay (or a switch) rarely close without "bouncing" a few times, large signal variations may be present at the output during the amplifier turn-on time. (Consider the effect of these variations if the amplifier were followed by a pulse- or level-detector circuit—the detector would probably "latch" each time the relay was energized.) Changes in the contact resistance can also affect the amount of signal reaching the base of the transistor.

A circuit that overcomes both of these disadvantages is shown in Fig. 7-2. The relay used in the previous circuit is replaced by a depletion-type IGFET, and the design takes advantage of the large ratio of off-to-on resistance of the IGFET. When the gate of Q1 is held at +10 V (approximately 20 percent above V_P plus the voltage at the source), the resistance from source to drain is very high (about 100 to 1000 megohms), and very little signal arrives at the base of Q2. When the control signal goes to zero volts, the drain-to-source resistance of the IGFET decreases to a low value (approximately one to two kilohms), and the input is effectively connected to the base of Q2. Since the gate of Q1 is isolated from the source-to-drain channel, the control signal is isolated from the input of Q2. While the on-off isolation obtained using an IGFET as the control device is not as good as that obtained when a relay is used, the ratio is still about 50 to 60 dB, perfectly adequate for most applications.

The amount of signal attenuation available in the off mode may be increased by adding an additional transistor to shunt

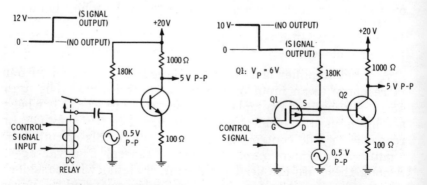

Fig. 7-1. A simple gated amplifier circuit configuration.

Fig. 7-2. A FET-controlled gated amplifier circuit.

the input signal to ground, as shown in Fig. 7-3. This is known as an L-pad attenuator and should be operated into a relatively high-impedance load (anywhere from about 10,000 ohms up). In operation, when Q1 is in the high-resistance state, Q2 is in the low-resistance state. Any signal getting through Q1 is shunted away from the base of Q3. When Q1 is in the low-resistance state (with the control voltage at −10 V), Q2 is in the high-resistance state and has very little effect on the input to Q3. Attenuation ratios of better than 80 dB may be achieved in this manner.

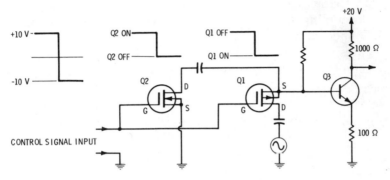

Fig. 7-3. Use of an L-pad attenuator.

Note that complementary IGFET's are used in the circuit of Fig. 7-3 so that one is off while the other is on. The effect of the control voltage may be reversed (so that the Q3 stage is gated on when the control voltage is positive and gated off when the control voltage is negative) by interchanging the p-channel IGFET, Q1, and the n-channel IGFET, Q2.

To use the circuits which have been discussed thus far effectively, some precautions must be taken. The attenuator circuit should be inserted into the amplifier circuit at a point where the signal level is as high as the attenuator can accept without causing distortion. Signal levels below about two volts peak-to-peak usually will be acceptable with most depletion-type IGFET's. Direct current (from bias networks) should be kept out of the attenuator through the use of suitable blocking capacitors. These blocking capacitors should be the same value as the interstage coupling capacitor used to couple into the gated stage. Finally, to avoid the noise and transient problems we are trying to eliminate through the use of a solid-state gate, the gate inputs must be adequately filtered (or "decoupled") from the control-voltage source, or control-voltage source noise will be amplified by the IGFET's and subsequently appear in the output of the gated stage. A simple RC network is usually adequate to perform this function.

Each of the on-off gating circuits illustrated in Figs. 7-1 through 7-3 may also be used as a variable-gain amplifier that may be controlled from a remote source. The circuit of Fig. 7-4, connected between a preamplifier and a power amplifier, will provide remote gain control without the need for shielded cable to run the actual audio lines to the remote-control point. The RC decoupling circuit discussed above is also shown in Fig. 7-4, connected between the wiper arm of potentiometer R1 and the gates of Q1 and Q2. The positive and negative control voltages can be borrowed from most modern solid-state stereo systems. As an alternative, a pair of 9-V transistor radio batteries may be used. The current drain of the circuit is extremely low (18 microamperes). A word of caution—be sure that the control voltage cannot exceed the maximum V_{GS} rating of the transistors used.

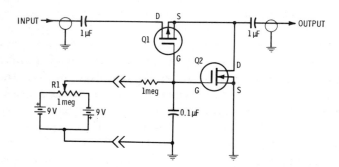

Fig. 7-4. A remote volume-control circuit.

VARIABLE-FEEDBACK AMPLIFIERS

Variable-feedback amplifiers are similar in operation to gated amplifiers, except that the control signal is derived from the output of the amplifier itself, rather than from an external control source.

The IGFET is a most versatile control device in variable-feedback amplifiers, as it was in the gated amplifier. An auto-

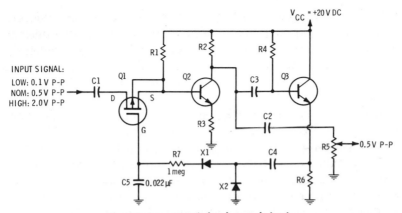

Fig. 7-5. An automatic level-control circuit.

matic level control is shown in Fig. 7-5. It can be used to avoid making adjustments in recording or public-address amplifier levels to compensate for varying input signal amplitudes. The circuit uses a p-channel depletion-type IGFET in a series attenuator configuration. The Q2 stage does the actual amplifying of the input signal, while Q1 controls the amount of input signal reaching the base of Q2. Emitter-follower stage Q3 isolates the rectifier, consisting of X1 and X2, from the output signal so that no distortion occurs when the signal is rectified and filtered. The rectified and filtered signal fed to the gate of Q1 is proportional to the output of Q2. As the output amplitude from Q2 tries to increase, the voltage at the gate of Q1 increases, raising the drain-to-source resistance and lowering the input signal amplitude to Q2. This action tends to keep the signal amplitude across potentiometer R5 constant, even though the input signal may vary.

This circuit would usually be inserted between a preamplifier and a power amplifier or between two stages in an amplifier system where the maximum signal level would be about 2 V peak-to-peak. Potentiometer R5 is adjusted so that the output level of the circuit at the nominal input level is equal to the input level. The level-control circuit then looks like a unity-gain amplifier, even though its overall gain increases to compensate for smaller input signals and decreases to reduce larger input signals to the nominal output level.

To obtain adequate gate signal voltage with some IGFET's, it may be necessary to operate the Q3 stage in the common-emitter configuration, rather than the common-collector configuration shown. It is also necessary to obtain a suitable RC time constant at the gate of Q1. If the product of R7 and C5 is too large, the circuit will operate too slowly, resulting in a "breathing" effect and poor instantaneous level control. If the product of R7 and C5 is too small, the circuit will try to compensate for variances in the shape rather than the size of the input signal.

Since the gate current required by Q1 is negligible, R7 should be made large in relation to C5, and the product (the RC time constant) should be adjusted for the best operation. A time constant of about 100 milliseconds works well in high-fidelity applications, while a time constant of 20 to 50 milliseconds is usually adequate for most voice or low-fidelity (cassette, ham radio, etc.) applications. The circuit of Fig. 7-5 has a 22-millisecond time constant.

It is not necessary to insert the controlling transistor in series with the input to the amplifying transistor. Fig. 7-6 shows a variation of the level-control circuit using an n-channel depletion-type IGFET that varies the effect of C_E, the emitter bypass capacitor of the Q1 stage, to control overall voltage gain. When the input signal is at the nominal value (in the middle of its dynamic range), the negative voltage at the gate of Q2 keeps Q2 about halfway between full-on and full-off. Potentiometer R4 is adjusted so that the gain from input to output is equal to one. If the input signal amplitude increases, Q2 is biased further into the depletion region by the increasingly negative voltage at its gate. As its drain-to-source re-

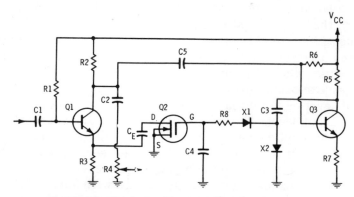

Fig. 7-6. A level control using a "variable bypass capacitor."

sistance increases, the effect of C_E is diminished, increasing the degenerative feedback effect of R3 and reducing the voltage gain of the stage. Should the input signal decrease, C_E is effectively connected across R3 through a low resistance, by-passing it and attempting to keep the voltage across R4 constant.

The same comments about the amount of gate-signal voltage required and the gate-signal time constant that were made about the circuit of Fig. 7-5 are applicable to this circuit. The circuit of Fig. 7-6 does have an advantage over the circuit which uses a series control device—the signal excursions across the emitter resistor are usually less than the excursions at the input to the stage. The signal excursions at the emitter tend to be rather constant because they are also controlled by the gain of the stage. This allows the circuit of Fig. 7-6 to handle higher peak-to-peak signal levels without distortion than the circuit of Fig. 7-5 can handle.

TRIGGERED OSCILLATORS

Another interesting circuit, useful in the generation of musical or percussion sounds (such as a bass drum or tom-tom) is the triggered oscillator. It is basically an ordinary phase-shift oscillator circuit which has been modified to produce an output that dies away at a controlled rate after an input trigger has caused it to start oscillating. One configuration of this circuit is illustrated in Fig. 7-7. Resistor R_E is adjusted so that

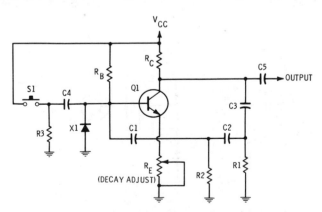

Fig. 7-7. A triggered oscillator circuit.

the circuit gain is just below that required for continuous oscillation. When switch S1 is closed, a pulse is applied to the base of Q1 through C4, shocking the circuit into oscillation. The oscillations die out a short time later, and the resulting output resembles that of a percussion instrument being struck. Resistor R3 and diode X1 provide a discharge path for C4 when S1 is released so that the circuit may be retriggered. The time constant of C4 and R3 determines how soon the circuit may be retriggered after S1 is opened. The decay characteristics (how long it takes for the oscillations to die away) are controlled by R_E.

The phase-shift oscillator portion of the circuit is designed in the conventional manner. The frequency of oscillation that is appropriate for the instrument being simulated is found experimentally by changing the values of C1 through C3. If thirteen such circuits are designed and tuned to the frequencies of the chromatic musical scale, a miniature xylophone or music box can be created. The trigger switches can be mounted behind a homemade keyboard—even doorbell buttons will work.

Another version of this same circuit, triggered this time in the emitter circuit, is shown in Fig. 7-8. This circuit has the advantage of a more controllable on time, since it will continue to oscillate until the current through C4 is no longer able to keep transistor Q2 turned on, bypassing R_E. Diode X1 is necessary to provide enough V_{CE} for Q2, to allow adequate collector current so that R_E is effectively shunted to ground when the circuit is triggered. The time constant R3, R4, and

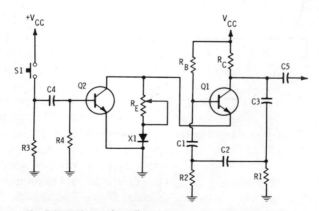

Fig. 7-8. A triggered oscillator circuit with controlled on time.

C4 determines how soon the circuit may be retriggered. The size of C4, coupled with R4 and the base-current requirements of Q2, determines the on time of the circuit.

ACTIVE FILTERS

Another class of circuits that may be derived from the phase-shift or twin-T oscillator is the active-filter category. These circuits may be designed either to amplify or attenuate a specific frequency, depending on whether positive or negative feedback is employed.

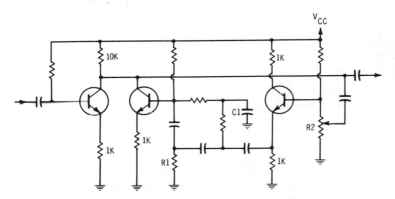

Fig. 7-9. An active bandpass filter circuit.

The simplest active filter used to amplify a specific frequency, while attenuating frequencies on either side of that frequency, is the phase-shift or twin-T oscillator adjusted just below the point of oscillation. When an input signal at (or near) the resonant frequency is applied to the circuit, an output is present. Signals too far away from the center frequency are attenuated. The single-stage filter has the disadvantage, however, of having poor selectivity (the ability to reject or accept signals close to its center frequency). This problem may be overcome by using additional stages which provide the proper gain and impedance matching to improve circuit performance.

Two practical circuits are shown in Figs. 7-9 and 7-10. The circuit of Fig. 7-9 is the bandpass type, while the circuit of Fig. 7-10 is the band-stop type. The center frequencies are calculated using the twin-T formula from Chapter 5. Notice that the only difference in the circuits is the feedback-signal mode (positive at the center frequency for Fig. 7-9 and negative at the center frequency for Fig. 7-10).

The stages are interconnected as shown, so that the frequency-determining network is fed from a low-impedance source and loaded by a high-impedance source, the ideal situation for most RC networks. The exact center frequency may be trimmed by adjusting either R1 or C1 (or both) in either circuit. The proper adjustment of R2 in the circuit of Fig. 7-9 is the point just below where the circuit oscillates. In the circuit of Fig. 7-10, R2 should be adjusted to obtain the best null (lowest output voltage at the center frequency).

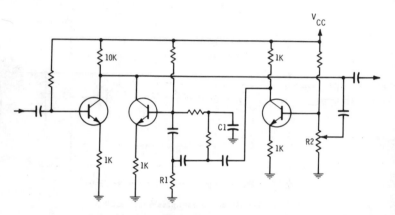

Fig. 7-10. An active band-stop, or notch, filter circuit.

These circuits have useful applications. If three or four of the bandpass filter outputs are connected to separate lamp-driver SCR or triac circuits (while all four bandpass filter inputs are connected to a music source), a color organ light show can be created. Each lamp will light at a different frequency. The result is both novel and entertaining. This is shown in block diagram form in Fig. 7-11. The band-stop filter of Fig. 7-10 can be used as the heart of a distortion analyzer, as shown in the block diagram of Fig. 7-12. The output from the filter, as read on the meter, consists only of the distortion introduced by the amplifier under test, since the center (test) frequency has been removed.

If it is necessary to create a high-pass or low-pass filter, rather than a bandpass or notch filter, the twin-T network may be replaced with a simple RC network (Fig. 7-13). Be sure to

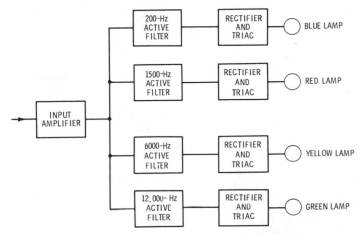

Fig. 7-11. Block diagram of a four-channel color organ.

observe the proper feedback voltage polarity, or the circuit will operate exactly opposite to the desired mode of operation.

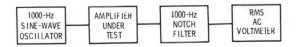

Fig. 7-12. Block diagram of a distortion analyzer.

VOLTAGE-CONTROLLED OSCILLATORS

If it is desired to convert a voltage change to a frequency change, the voltage-controlled oscillator is usually the best choice. A voltage-controlled oscillator can even be used to convert a digital counter into a digital voltmeter, although this method is a bit crude and is somewhat nonlinear.

Perhaps the simplest voltage-controlled oscillator is the circuit of Fig. 7-14. The circuit shown is a simple PUT re-

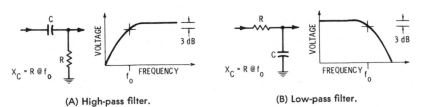

(A) High-pass filter.   (B) Low-pass filter.

Fig. 7-13. Simple RC-filter configuration.

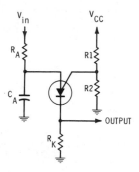

Fig. 7-14. A simple voltage-controlled oscillator.

laxation oscillator that has the timing resistor tied to the varying voltage that is to be converted to frequency variations. If the voltage at the top of R_A is raised, capacitor C_A charges to the V_P of the PUT faster than it did previously. The output frequency (across R_K) increases. If the voltage at the top of R_A is lowered, it takes longer to charge C_A, and the output frequency is reduced.

The changes in frequency of the circuit in Fig. 7-14 do not correspond linearly to the changes in input voltage, since the charge time of C_A follows the typical exponential capacitor curve. If C_A is charged from a constant-current source that can be varied, much better linearity can be obtained. Resistor R_A can be replaced with a FET constant-current source. The FET current can be varied by changing the value of its source resistor. If a light-dependent resistor is used as the source resistor and the varying input voltage is applied to the lamp that feeds the LDR, the output frequency can be varied. To maintain an adequate input impedance for the input voltage

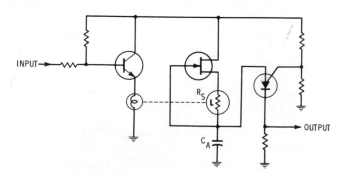

Fig. 7-15. An improved voltage-controlled oscillator.

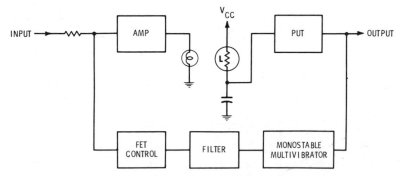

Fig. 7-16. Block diagram of a PUT voltage-controlled oscillator with feedback.

source, a common-collector amplifier stage can be incorporated. A PUT voltage-controlled oscillator circuit with all of these improvements is shown in Fig. 7-15.

The linearity of the circuit can be improved even further through the addition of a frequency-to-voltage converter the output of which is used as a feedback source for the input. A block diagram of such an arrangement is shown in Fig. 7-16, where a monostable multivibrator is used as the frequency-to-voltage converter. While the negative feedback applied from output to input will reduce the amount of frequency change realized for a given input voltage change, it will improve the linearity of the ratio $\Delta V/\Delta f$, where Δf is the output-frequency change and ΔV is the input-voltage change.

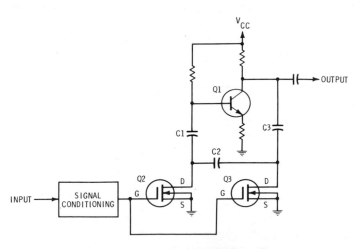

Fig. 7-17. A FET-controlled phase-shift oscillator.

Another circuit usable for voltage-to-frequency conversion incorporates two IGFET's to trim the frequency of a phase-shift oscillator. This is shown in Fig. 7-17. The block marked "signal conditioning" is used to convert the input signal to the voltage levels required by the IGFET gates and should be designed accordingly. The capacitor values for the oscillator center frequency should be calculated for the nominal IGFET drain-to-source resistance.

The circuit of Fig. 7-17 is shown primarily to illustrate an additional voltage-controlled oscillator. The limited dynamic range of the circuit makes it impractical for most applications. (Oscillations will cease altogether if the IGFET drain-to-source resistance is too large or too small.)

NOISE SOURCES

While noise is an undesirable and difficult-to-eliminate phenomenon in almost all circuit designs, it does have its place. For example, if the output of a triggered oscillator (tuned to sound like a tom-tom) is mixed with the proper amount of noise, the result (amplified and converted to sound with a speaker) is the sound of a snare drum. The type of noise used is important, however, since noise comes in a great many varieties. The type of noise used most often in electronic circuits is *white noise*. This is noise which is quite evenly distributed over the entire frequency spectrum. Coincidentally, white noise is relatively easy to generate. A great many devices create a small amount of white noise when stressed by operating circuit potentials. The bipolar transistor and the zener diode are the best sources of white noise. For these devices to operate effectively as noise sources, it is necessary to operate them in the *avalanche,* or reverse-breakdown, mode, with suitable current limiting to preclude destruction of the device.

A zener diode is usually operated at the knee of its characteristic curve to obtain the best noise output. The series resistor (Fig. 7-18A) is adjusted for maximum noise output. The bipolar transistor is usually connected so that its base-emitter junction is reverse biased into the breakdown region (Fig. 7-18B). Here again, the series resistor is trimmed for best noise output.

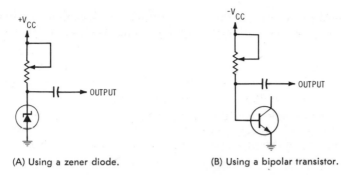

(A) Using a zener diode.   (B) Using a bipolar transistor.

Fig. 7-18. Solid-state noise sources.

If the white noise generated by either circuit of Fig. 7-18 is to be used, it must be properly gated or amplified. If white noise is simply amplified and fed to a speaker or earphones, it may have a relaxing and/or pain-relieving effect. (Several hundred dentists have augmented Novocain anesthesia with white noise.)

If white noise is to be used in conjunction with a triggered oscillator (creating the sound of a snare drum, an application mentioned earlier); it should be amplified by a gated amplifier the output of which is a "pulse" of noise. A circuit to perform this function is shown in Fig. 7-19.

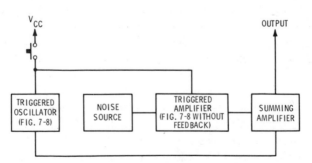

Fig. 7-19. Block diagram of a snare-drum sound generator.

SUMMARY

The circuits described and illustrated in this chapter were selected to show the range of special-purpose analog circuits available to the circuit designer. They are, of course, by no means a complete listing of all of the circuits available for use in a system design. There are variations of and modifications to each of the circuits that will make them perform exactly the required function.

If the design of a special-purpose circuit is approached in a logical manner, after careful definition of the input stimulus and output response requirements, a circuit can be developed that will at least come close to the requirements. Tailoring of the individual circuit components and parameters should be sufficient to make any circuit function almost perfectly.

CHAPTER 8

Digital and
Switching Circuits

Digital circuits, in contrast to analog circuits, have only two input (and output) conditions—*on* and *off* (or low voltage and high voltage, current and no current, etc.). They are not ordinarily required to discern or process minor signal variations. If an on/off input must be obtained from some nonelectrical impulse or small signal variation, an analog circuit with an output that is high or low, depending on its input, should be designed to feed the digital circuit. The digital circuits can then operate on the inputs, make decisions based on the number and state of the inputs, and provide on/off control signals as outputs.

LOGIC CIRCUITS

Most digital circuits are called logic circuits. These are circuit configurations that make logical, predictable, and repeatable decisions. Logic circuitry is based on the binary numbering system, in which only the numbers 0 and 1 are used. Since digital circuits have only two states, off and on, this numbering system is tailor-made for them. If we make binary 0 equal to a low output voltage state and call it NO, while letting binary 1 equal a high output voltage state and calling it YES, we can create logic networks to give us yes or no answers (in the form of electrical signals) about the states of the inputs.

The two basic decision-making logic circuits, the AND gate and the OR gate, are shown implemented with switches and lamps in Fig. 8-1. The inputs are labeled "A" and "B," and the output in each case is labeled "Q." The input is 0 if the switch is open and 1 if the switch is closed. The output is 0 if the lamp is off and 1 if the lamp is on. Below each circuit is its equation in Boolean algebra, the mathematics of logic circuitry. In Boolean algebra, the dot ($\cdot$) is read "and." The plus sign ($+$) is read "or." The output of the AND gate of Fig. 8-1A will be high (1) if both inputs are high (1). The output of the OR gate of Fig. 8-1B will be high (1) if one or both of its inputs are high (1).

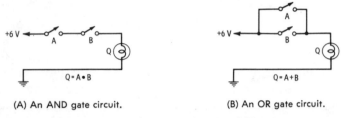

(A) An AND gate circuit.   (B) An OR gate circuit.

Fig. 8-1. Logic configurations of AND and OR gates.

The schematic symbols and truth tables for each of the various logic circuits in common use today are illustrated in Fig. 8-2. The AND and OR gates have already been discussed. The buffer gate (Fig. 8-2C) is a circuit used to increase the *fan-out* (drive capability) of a signal. Its input state is equal to its output state.

The symbols in Fig. 8-2D through Fig. 8-2F are the NAND, NOR and inverter, respectively. The bar over the input term(s) ($Q = \overline{A}$ for the inverter, as an example) is read "not." Note that one of the peculiarities of Boolean algebra applied to NAND and NOR logic elements is that the equations for the circuits may be written two ways. With the bar over the entire input term (Fig. 8-2D), the equation is read "Q will be high if (A and B) is not high." If the bar is placed over the Q term, rather than over the A $\cdot$ B term ($\overline{Q} = A \cdot B$), the equation reads "Q will be not high (low) if (A and B) is high." When the bar is over the whole term ($Q = \overline{A \cdot B}$), it must be remembered that the bar covers the dot, too. Then, when the bar over the input terms is split up (as $Q = \overline{A} + \overline{B}$, rather than over the

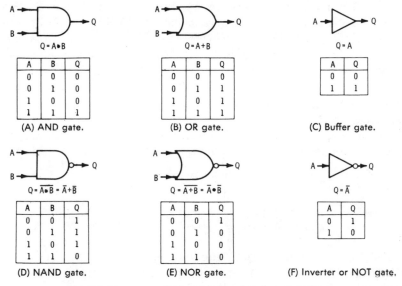

Fig. 8-2. The common logic symbols and their truth tables.

entire term), the dot is replaced by the plus sign, and the equation is read "Q will be high if A or B is not high." This is because the bar originally covered the dot (making it a "not" AND), and the conversion is a (+) without a bar, meaning OR. When the bar is not over the entire input term, it cannot be moved to the output term. While $Q = \overline{A \cdot B}$ equals $\overline{Q} = A \cdot B$, $Q = \overline{A} + \overline{B}$ does not equal $\overline{Q} = A + B$. Some mental practice with these manipulations, using the truth tables as guides, will soon make it quite easy, rather than confusing, to choose the correct gate function for a specific task.

There is no practical restriction on the number of inputs that may be applied to an AND or an OR gate. To keep the illustrations simple, two or three inputs are used most often in the circuit descriptions which follow. The number of inputs (fan-in) can be increased when needed as long as adequate voltage and current are available to make the gates operate properly.

The diagram of Fig. 8-3 illustrates one method used to select the logic circuit required for a given task. The input stimulus and output response are defined, in truth-table form, in terms of 1's and 0's. Then the required truth table is compared against the known truth tables until a match is found. Some

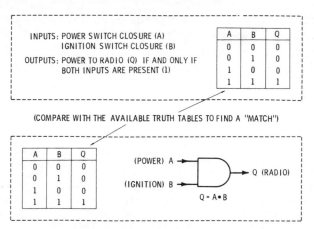

Fig. 8-3. Simple example of logic-element selection.

designs require more than one logic element. This is illustrated in Fig. 8-4, where the input/output relationship is defined in equation form so that the logic elements may be selected. Note that there is usually more than one way to implement logic functions. The idea is to simplify them as far as possible, as in Fig. 8-4.

INTERFACE REQUIREMENTS

If logic circuits were formed using only switches or relays, they would be large, slow, and almost impossible to use for complicated logic systems. Digital circuits of all types lend themselves well, however, to implementation with diodes and transistors. The diode has only two states (off and on), and

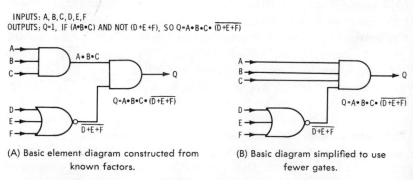

Fig. 8-4. Multiple element selection from equations.

the transistor may easily be operated (in the cutoff and saturated modes) as an electronic switch.

When a number of logic circuits are to be used in a system, it is helpful to have a "standard" input and output interface. If each gate input requires a fixed amount of voltage and current and each gate output can provide a certain amount of voltage and current, a simple set of rules may be put forth for the gate interconnections.

The schematic for an AND gate constructed with a resistor and diodes is shown in Fig. 8-5. The inputs need not supply any current (except diode leakage) when they are in the high state. With all three inputs high, there is no path for current through the resistor, so the output is at +5 V. If any one input is low, it will *sink* approximately 5 mA and maintain the voltage at Q at a level equal to the drop across the diode. If the other inputs are made low, the current will be shared by all three diodes. The output voltage will remain at a level equal to the smallest diode forward drop.

The schematic for an OR gate constructed with diodes and a resistor is shown in Fig. 8-6. In this case the inputs do supply current (approximately 5 mA) when in the high state. If any one input is high, the output is high and the other input diodes are reverse biased. If all three inputs are high, the input current will be shared by the three diodes. The output voltage in this case is 0 V for the low state and about +4.3 V for the high state.

If each of the circuits discussed so far is used individually, it will work well. Consider what happens when we begin to connect them together, however. If we use the outputs of three AND gates as the inputs to another AND gate, the output voltage levels of the second AND gate will be +1.4 V for the low state and +5 V for the high state. If we continue to add gates,

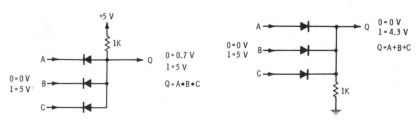

Fig. 8-5. A diode AND gate.   Fig. 8-6. A diode OR gate.

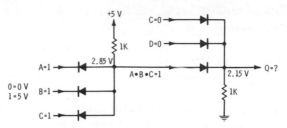

Fig. 8-7. A diode AND gate feeding diode OR gate.

we eventually have no signal change at the output to denote a high or a low.

If we connect the outputs of three OR gates to the inputs of another OR gate, the output voltage levels of the second OR gate will be 0 V (low) and +3.6 V (high). If we continue to add gates, there is again eventually no voltage change at the final output to denote a high or a low.

An examination of the effect of feeding the AND gate of Fig. 8-5 from the OR gate of Fig. 8-6 shows that the interconnected circuit will work properly. The OR gate inputs supply current to raise its output to +4.3 V. This voltage is high enough to allow the AND gate output to rise to about +5 V. Should the OR gate be fed from the AND gate, however, both gates cease to function properly. This is illustrated in Fig. 8-7. The AND gate output, when high, must supply current to the OR gate resistor. The OR gate output can go no higher than approximately +2 V.

So while each of the simple diode logic gates shown is perfectly adequate in certain uses, a general-purpose, standard interface circuit usable for multielement designs is still required. The solution to this problem is one or more transistor gain stages that require a standard input and provide a standard output, regardless of what other gates they are connected to.

The development of a family of gates types (AND, OR, NAND, NOR, buffer and inverter) using diodes and transistors will allow the fan-in and fan-out to be specified for the following four voltage levels:

V_{OL}—The maximum output voltage in the low state
V_{OH}—The minimum output voltage in the high state
V_{IL}—The maximum input voltage that will assure a low at the gate output

V_{IH}—The minimum input voltage that will insure a high at the gate output

As long as V_{OL} is less than V_{IL} and V_{OH} is greater than V_{IH}, the gates will all function correctly. The number of inputs that may be connected to an output while maintaining the above inequalities can then be specified. If more gates need to be driven from an output, a buffer can be added to extend the fan-out.

SATURATED-AMPLIFIER DESIGN

The design of saturated amplifiers in this section will include the input gate structure, since the gate structure must be treated as an integral part of the amplifier if it is to operate properly.

Fig. 8-8 shows the output portion of a transistor stage. The $V_{CE(sat)}$ of the transistor is the factor that determines V_{OL}, while the resistor value determines how many loads may be connected to the output while still maintaining V_{OH}. If the stage output must provide current to its loads, the resistor value must be relatively small and the transistor must sink any load current plus the current through the resistor. If the stage output must supply only minimal current to its loads, V_{OH} will not vary greatly, and the value of the resistor may be much larger than the value required when the stage must be the source of output current; in this case, little power is wasted in the transistor and resistor.

It appears then, that the stage output should sink current from its load in the on (output = 0) state for best efficiency. This criterion determines the structure of the input gates feeding the transistor stage. The AND gate previously shown in Fig. 8-5 meets the zero-state sinking requirements that have

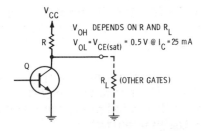

Fig. 8-8. Saturated amplifier output.

been decided upon. Fig. 8-9A shows one of the output stages feeding an AND gate diode and subsequently the transistor for its output. Note that if the $V_{CE(sat)}$ of Q1 is 0.5 V max, the diode drop is 0.7 V max, and the $V_{BE(sat)}$ of Q2 is 1 V max, Q2 may be on all the time. This problem may be solved by adding diode X1 to the circuit, as in Fig. 8-9B. The voltage at the anode of X1 can now approach $0.5 + 0.7 = 1.2$ V and Q2 will remain definitely off since $1.0 + 0.7 = 1.7$ V is required at the anode of X1 for base current to be established in Q2. Now V_{in} may approach one volt without turning the transistor on. The minimum input voltage to the gate for a high state must be at least 1.7 volts to insure that the input diodes are definitely off. If another diode drop is arbitrarily added (as a safety margin), the transistor output V_{OH} must be 2.4 volts, an easily attainable number if we choose $V_{CC} = 5$ V.

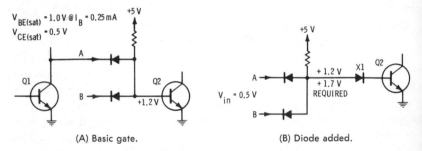

(A) Basic gate.   (B) Diode added.

Fig. 8-9. The AND gate input diode structure.

The circuit input and output impedances should be low to increase the circuit noise immunity. The input current to the base of the output transistor should be about four times the $I_{B(sat)}$ value to insure that the transistor is adequately turned on, even for abnormal values of I_C.

The input and output interface may be defined and the circuit values selected with the information now known. Fig. 8-10 shows the complete circuit with the important characteristics listed. (The circuit shown is a NAND gate, since the output is inverted.) Using $I_{B(sat)} = 0.25$ mA, R1 should supply 1 mA through X3 and Q1. Its value should be $(5 \text{ V} - 1.7 \text{ V})/1 \text{ mA} = 3.3K$, a standard value. When the input is connected to a gate output, the current is: $I = (5 \text{ V} - 0.7 \text{ V} - 0.5 \text{ V})/3.3K = 1.15$ mA. To insure adequate fan-out from the driving gate, assume that a "unit input load" (one input) $= 1.2$ mA.

If $I_{C(sat)}$ is 25 mA, as many as $25/1.2 = 20.8$ loads may be connected to a gate output. This leaves no margin for error and no current for R2. In practice, twenty gates will seldom need to be connected to a single driver. How many gates can be connected? Assume that the leakage that must be supplied by R2 is 50 microamperes maximum. If 20 gates are connected for a total current of $20 \times 50 = 1000$ $\mu A = 1$ mA, and V_{OH} is to be 2.4 V minimum, no more than 2.6 volts may be dropped across R2. Its value should then be R2 $= 2.6$ V$/1$ mA $= 2.6$K. Select a 2.7K standard value resistor.

When transistor Q1 is on, it will sink $(5$ V $- 0.5$ V$)/2.7$K $=$ 1.6 mA. That leaves approximately 23 mA for gate loads. This allows for a little over 19 gate loads, so, to provide a small margin for component variations and tolerances, make the "rule" eighteen "unit input loads" of 1.2 mA maximum connected to any gate output. Then V_{OH} will be about 2.6 V minimum, slightly above the minimum previously specified.

The gate shown in Fig. 8-10 is a NAND gate. To convert it to an AND gate, it is necessary only to invert the output. A suitable circuit is shown in Fig. 8-11. Resistor R should be chosen to supply the same 1 mA to Q2 as was supplied to the base of Q1 in the NAND gate. Its value should be $(5$ V $- 1$ V$)/1$ mA $=$ 4000 ohms. The nearest standard value, 3.9K, should work well.

We now have a NAND gate, an AND gate, an inverter (which is a NAND with one input), and a buffer (an AND with one input) of the same family which can be interconnected at will as long as the loading rule is not exceeded. The development of a compatible NOR and OR circuit will complete the family. The circuit of Fig. 8-12 is an OR gate compatible with the other circuits. The input resistor value is chosen so that the driving

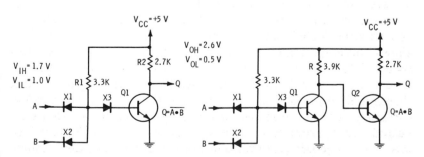

Fig. 8-10. A diode-transistor NAND gate.   Fig. 8-11. A diode-transistor AND gate.

gate sinks approximately 1.15 mA. Its value is $(5\text{ V} - 0.5\text{ V})/$ 1.15 mA = 3.9K. Resistor R_X prevents any leakage current from turning on Q1. A 100K resistor should be quite acceptable. The only restriction on how many inputs an OR gate (or a NOR gate) may have is that the $I_{B(\max)}$ of the input transistor may not be exceeded. For most circuits, a fan-in of four is more than adequate and will not normally exceed the device ratings. If more than four OR inputs are needed, two gates should be used, with the output of one gate connected to one of the inputs of the other gate.

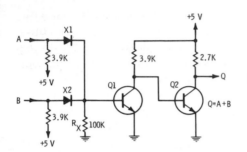

Fig. 8-12. A diode-transistor OR gate.

DIGITAL INTEGRATED CIRCUITS

The advent of the integrated circuit (IC) has made the use of discrete logic (such as that just described) unnecessary and impractical for all but the smallest logic systems. Integrated circuits that contain four two-input OR gates or six inverter circuits are available for the price of a single transistor, and all of the circuitry is contained in one small package.

There are many classes of digital IC's, but the two most popular seem to be the 7400 series of TTL (transistor-transistor logic) IC's and the various high-level DTL (diode-transistor logic) IC's. The TTL IC's operate from a 5-volt power supply, while the high-level DTL operates (usually) from a 12-volt supply.

The majority of manufacturers will be glad to supply data sheets on their families of digital IC's. Most IC's are available in small quantities from mail-order parts houses and industrial suppliers. It is important, when using IC's in a logic system, to stay within the same family of logic (TTL, DTL, etc.), so that interface problems will be avoided.

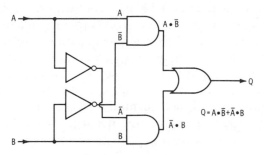

Fig. 8-13. Diagram of an exclusive-OR circuit.

It is convenient to use IC logic when functions more complex than the simple AND-OR logic must be performed. Figs. 8-13, 8-14, 8-15 and 8-16 illustrate some of the complex "web of decision" networks that may be constructed using the simple gates available in IC form.

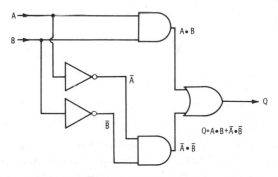

Fig. 8-14. Diagram of a coincidence detector circuit.

The circuit of Fig. 8-13 is called an exclusive-OR circuit. Its output is high if one input is high and the other input is low. If the A and B inputs were connected to two supposedly identical circuits, the Q output would go high to indicate that one of the circuits had changed state with respect to the other. The circuit of Fig. 8-14 is a coincidence detector. Its output is high when its inputs match (both 0 or both 1). The Q output of the majority detector of Fig. 8-15 will go high whenever 2 out of 3 (or more) of its inputs are high. A circuit constructed with this type of logic might be used to allow an electronic lock to be opened only when at least two different inputs (people) are present.

The circuit of Fig. 8-16 is used to eliminate the effects of switch contact bounce. As mentioned in Chapter 7, switch and relay contacts rarely close without "bouncing" from an open to a closed position a few times. When switch S1 is moved to position A, the Q output goes high. The high Q input to the B gate causes its output ($\overline{Q}$) to go low, keeping the A gate output high. Since this switching action occurs in microseconds or nanoseconds, the Q output is locked high before the switch contacts can bounce, milliseconds after the first closure. When the switch is moved to position B, the Q output goes low and a similar course of events takes place.

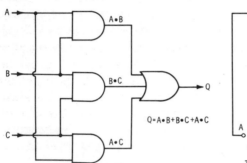

Fig. 8-15. Diagram of a "two-out-of-three" majority detector circuit.

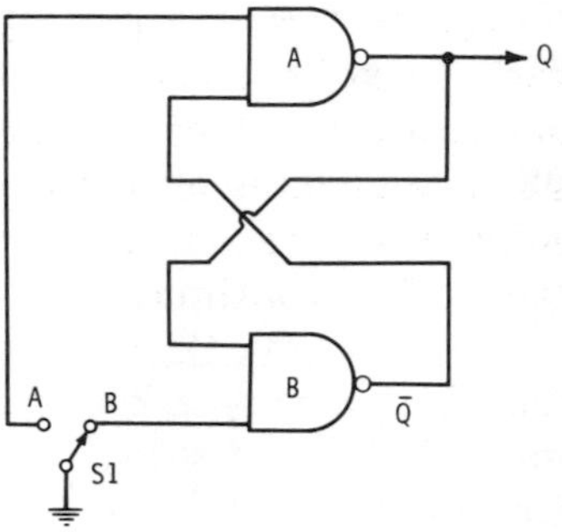

Fig. 8-16. Diagram of a switch-contact debouncing circuit.

There are, of course, many more IC types available that may be interconnected to form a great many more decision-making and counting circuits. These IC's include monostable and bistable multivibrators (whose discrete forms are discussed in the next section). A good logic design handbook should be consulted if difficulty is encountered in trying to design a circuit to perform a specific task. It takes a complete book to do the subject justice, and we have only a portion of a chapter.

BISTABLE AND MONOSTABLE MULTIVIBRATORS

The bistable multivibrator is a circuit that will remain in one of two stable states, indefinitely, until caused to switch to the other stable state by some external stimulus. The basic circuit of the "counting" flip-flop, which changes state each time its input is triggered, is shown in Fig. 8-17. The circuit is called a counting flip-flop since the number of positive or negative output transitions at either collector is equal to half the number of input positive or negative transitions. The flip-flop will then divide the input frequency by two. If an additional flip-flop is fed from the output of the first flip-flop, its output will be the input frequency divided by four. Each additional stage divides the frequency by two.

Assume that the circuit of Fig. 8-17 is in a stable state with Q1 on and Q2 off. Transistor Q1 is held on by the current through R_{T2} from the collector of Q2. Transistor Q2 is held off because of the voltage across R_E. (There is not enough current through R_{T1} with the collector voltage of Q1 at $V_{RE} + V_{CE(sat)}$ to forward bias Q2. The base of Q2 is essentially reverse biased through R_{B2}.) When a pulse is applied to the input, it has no effect on transistor Q1. It does turn on transistor Q2. The falling collector voltage of Q2 causes the Q1 collector voltage to rise, since Q1 has less base current. This regenerative effect continues until the flip-flop assumes a stable state with Q1 off and Q2 on. Another input pulse upsets the circuit equilibrium and causes the circuit to flip back to its original state. This flip-flop action continues as long as trigger pulses are supplied.

The design of a bistable flip-flop is relatively straightforward. The resistance of $R_{C1} = R_{C2}$ should be chosen to drop

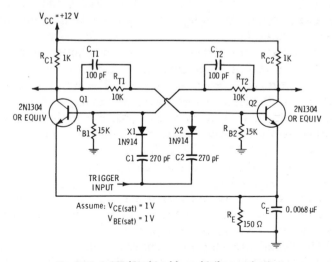

Fig. 8-17. A 200-kHz bistable multivibrator circuit.

approximately $V_{CC} - V_{RE}$ at $I_{C(sat)}$. The magnitude of V_{RE} is usually chosen to be between one and two volts, so R_E equals approximately 1.5 $V/I_{C(sat)}$. The value of $R_{T1} = R_{T2}$ is chosen so that approximately $I_{B(sat)}$ will flow with $V_{CC} - V_{BE(sat)} - V_{RE}$ dropped across it. The value of $R_{B1} = R_{B2}$ is chosen to maintain the transistor base at approximately V_{RE} when $R_{T1} = R_{T2}$ is being fed from $V_{RE} + V_{CE(sat)}$. The trigger capacitors (C_{T1} and C_{T2}) are normally about 100 pF, and C1 and C2 are usually 2.5 to 3 times $C_{T1} = C_{T2}$. If the transistors used have low values of beta, the capacitor values may need to be increased. Capacitor C_E should be approximately $1/R_E$ microfarads.

An example should serve to illustrate the procedure. Assume that $V_{CC} = +12$ V dc, the $I_{C(sat)}$ of Q1 and Q2 is 10 mA, and $I_{B(sat)} = 1$ mA. For these conditions, $R_{C1} = R_{C2}$ should be (12 V − 1.5 V)/10 mA = 1050 ohms. Use a standard 1000-ohm resistor. The value of R_E should be 1.5 V/10 mA = 150 ohms. Resistors R_{T1} and R_{T2} are chosen so that an $I_{B(sat)}$ of 1 mA flows at 12 V − 1 V − 1.5 V = 9.5 volts. Then $R_{T1} = R_{T2} = 9.5$ V/ 1 mA = 9500 ohms. A standard 10K resistor should suffice. To calculate $R_{B1} = R_{B2}$, assume that the collector of the on transistor is at $V_{RE} + V_{CE(sat)} = 2.5$ V. To maintain the base voltage at approximately V_{RE}, or 1.5 V, $R_{T1} = R_{T2}$ must drop about 1 volt. The current is then 1 V/10K ohms = 0.1 mA. Resistors R_{B1} and R_{B2} should drop 1.5 V at this 0.1 mA value, so they should be 1.5 V/0.1 mA = 15K resistors. The typical capacitor values shown in Fig. 8-17 should allow operation of the flip-flop in excess of 200 kilohertz.

The monostable multivibrator puts out a pulse of a specific amplitude and width each time it receives an input trigger pulse. It is commonly used to "stretch" the width of an input pulse or to standardize several different pulse widths. The design of a monostable multivibrator (see Fig. 8-18) follows the same general lines as the design for a bistable multivibrator. Resistors R_E, R_{C1}, R_{C2}, R_T, and R_{B1} are chosen in exactly the same fashion as they were for the bistable circuit, as is capacitor C_E. Resistor R_{B2} is chosen to allow $I_{B(sat)}$ to flow with $V_{CC} - V_{BE} - V_{RE}$ across it. Capacitor C_T determines the output pulse width at the collector of Q2. The capacitance of $C_T = T/$ 0.69 R_B, where T is the output pulse width in seconds. When fairly long time intervals are required that put the value of C_T above about 1 μF, be sure to use a high-quality capacitor. A leaky capacitor will make the circuit operate erratically, if it operates at all.

When either the bistable or the monostable multivibrator must drive resistive loads connected to ground, the effect of the external load resistor on the collector voltage of the off transistor should be taken into account. This is analogous to

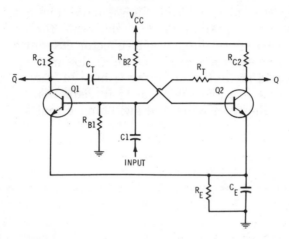

Fig. 8-18. A typical monostable multivibrator circuit.

taking R_L into account when computing stage gain in an analog circuit. Most circuits will work well until you connect them together. The effects of their environment must be considered.

SUMMARY

The circuits discussed in this chapter form the basis for the most powerful and complex digital computers in existence today. Digital techniques, such as the phase-locked loop, are even taking over such jobs as fm stereo-multiplex decoding, which previously used analog circuits.

For small projects, discrete diode or diode-transistor logic gates may usually be used. When projects grow in complexity, it is usually simpler and cheaper to use some of the many digital integrated circuits available today. The principles of saturated amplifier design may be applied to control logic and drivers (such as relay and lamp drivers) as long as device ratings are given careful consideration.

The flip-flop may be interconnected directly and with logic gating to perform a number of functions, including such things as dividing by any number between 2 and 10 (or more, using combination counters), preventing switch and relay contact bounce, and even storing information in the form of binary data bits.

The monostable multivibrator may be used to gate an analog amplifier (to aid in making high-fidelity tone-burst measurements, for example) or used as the basis for an automobile tachometer (where the average collector current of one of the transistors causes movement on an analog meter).

The world of digital circuitry is here to stay, and to grow. This chapter has provided a brief introduction to those areas known as digital circuits and switching circuits.

CHAPTER 9

Analog
Integrated Circuits

Just as the digital IC has rapidly replaced discrete logic circuitry, the various analog IC's are finding a larger place in today's solid-state world. Since it takes no more space to package a complete analog system than to package a single transistor, fully integrated amplifiers, voltage regulators, and other more special-purpose circuits can be fabricated in a single unit. The resultant decrease in parts count when discrete circuitry is replaced by an IC is usually enough to justify the higher cost of the IC. There are even integrated-circuit packages that act as power amplifiers with as much as fifteen watts of output power.

OPERATIONAL AMPLIFIERS

The operational amplifier, or op amp, was originally developed to perform mathematical operations (addition, subtraction, multiplication, etc.) in analog computers. The basic characteristics of an operational amplifier are a very high open-loop gain (the voltage gain without feedback), high input impedance (usually greater than a megohm), and a low output impedance (usually less than a hundred ohms).

Typical of the high-quality op amps available today is the μA741, the schematic symbol and pin connections of which are

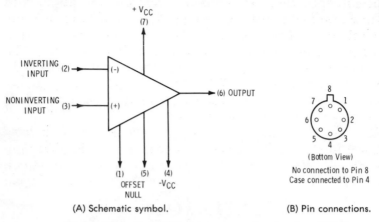

(A) Schematic symbol.

(B) Pin connections.

(Bottom View)
No connection to Pin 8
Case connected to Pin 4

Fig. 9-1. Schematic symbol and pin connections for the µA741 IC.

shown in Fig. 9-1. The open-loop gain is a minimum of 50,000, the input impedance is typically about two megohms, and the output impedance is approximately 75 ohms. The µA741 will operate with power-supply voltages of from ±5 to ±15 volts, and its output is short-circuit proof.

The op amp is operated in one of two modes—either as an inverting amplifier (input to the (−) terminal) or as a non-inverting amplifier (input to the (+) terminal). Negative feedback is always connected from the output to the inverting (−) input. The ratio of the feedback resistor to the input series resistor (R_f and R_s, respectively, in Fig. 9-2) determines the "closed-loop" voltage gain of the amplifier. The resistor in the noninverting input leg is equal in value to the parallel combination of R_f and R_s.

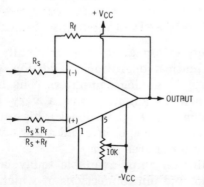

Fig. 9-2. A simple operational-amplifier circuit.

The 10K potentiometer connected from pin 1 to pin 5, with its wiper arm tied to the $-V_{CC}$ supply, is used to "null out" any offset voltage. (Offset voltage is the difference between input and output voltage with both inputs held at zero volts.) The 10K potentiometer is adjusted so that the output is zero volts with both inputs grounded. When the op amp is used as an ac-coupled (rather than direct-coupled) amplifier, the offset null-ing terminals can simply be left open.

The operational amplifier obeys all of the feedback laws discussed in Chapter 4. When it is operated in the inverting mode, shunt voltage feedback is applied to the input terminal. This results in a low input impedance (approximately equal to R_s) and a voltage gain defined by the formula:

$$A_{Vf} = \frac{R_f}{R_s} \qquad \text{(Eq. 9-1)}$$

The schematic for an inverting amplifier using the μA741 op amp is shown in Fig. 9-3. Also shown is a chart of the closed-loop voltage gain of the circuit for several typical combina-tions of R_f and R_s. Note that the upper frequency limit (UFL) of the circuit decreases as the amount of feedback is decreased (to increase the closed-loop gain). This phenomenon, which also obeys the feedback laws, restricts the gain of practical cir-cuits to a value well below the open-loop gain of the op amp. For an audio amplifier with a response from zero to 20 kHz, the gain can be no larger than 50 (approximately). If the gain is increased beyond this value, the frequency response begins to suffer. The actual usable bandwidth for a given closed-loop gain may be obtained from the chart of frequency versus open-loop gain on the data sheet for the op amp being used.

The schematic for the noninverting amplifier configuration is shown in Fig. 9-4, along with a chart tabulating typical R_f

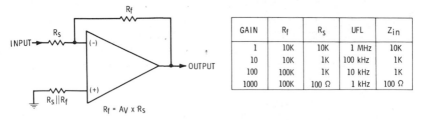

GAIN	R_f	R_s	UFL	Z_{in}
1	10K	10K	1 MHz	10K
10	10K	1K	100 kHz	1K
100	100K	1K	10 kHz	1K
1000	100K	100 Ω	1 kHz	100 Ω

$R_f = A_V \times R_s$

Fig. 9-3. The inverting operational-amplifier circuit.

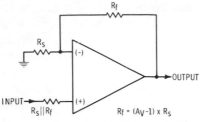

GAIN	R_f	R_s	UFL	Z_{in}
1	0	*	1 MHz	600 meg
10	9K	1K	100 kHz	400 meg
100	9.9K	100 Ω	10 kHz	250 meg
1000	99.9K	100 Ω	1 kHz	80 meg

*MAY BE ANY VALUE, USUALLY INFINITE
(R_s NOT USED AT ALL)

Fig. 9-4. The noninverting operational-amplifier circuit.

and R_s values. Note that while the input impedance still decreases with increased gain, it is much greater than the value obtained when the inverting configuration is used. This is because no feedback is applied directly to the input terminal. The formula for the closed-loop voltage gain of an op amp in the noninverting configuration is:

$$A_{Vf} = \frac{R_f + R_s}{R_s} \qquad \text{(Eq. 9-2)}$$

The reason for the difference between the voltage-gain formulas for the inverting and noninverting configurations, although it might appear mysterious at first, is really quite simple. If the equations above are converted to formulas for R_f, they become:

$$R_f = A_V R_s \qquad \text{(Eq. 9-3)}$$

for the inverting amplifier, and

$$R_f = (A_V - 1) R_s \qquad \text{(Eq. 9-4)}$$

for the noninverting amplifier. The difference in these equations is the difference between A_V and $A_V - 1$. If you examine both circuits, you will see that in the inverting configuration the input is applied to the feedback summing point. This signal is missing from the feedback summing point when the amplifier is used in the noninverting configuration. This signal nonpresence is represented by the number 1 in equation 9-4. This makes the calculation of R_f and R_s a bit more tedious, but the increase in input impedance is usually well worth the small extra effort.

The op amp can be used to replace discrete circuitry in almost any application. It may be used as a signal source, as depicted in Figs. 9-5 and 9-6. It may be used as a "signal

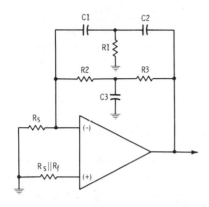

Fig. 9-5. A twin-T oscillator using
the op amp.

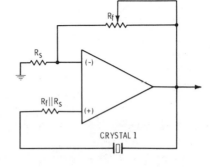

Fig. 9-6. A crystal-controlled operational-
amplifier oscillator.

modifier," as shown in Figs. 9-7 and 9-8, or it may be used as a
signal detector as illustrated in Fig. 9-9.

The circuit of Fig. 9-5 uses the op amp in the inverting configuration. The feedback resistor (R2 + R3 with R2 = R3) is
selected so that $R_f/R_s = 40$ and is part of the twin-T network.
The result is a sine-wave oscillator, the frequency of which is
determined by the values of C1 through C3 and R1 through R3.
In Fig. 9-6, a crystal provides positive feedback, at its resonant
frequency, to the noninverting input of the op amp. Feedback
resistor R_f is adjusted so that enough loop gain is available to
sustain oscillations.

The circuit of Fig. 9-7 is called an integrator. It converts the
square wave applied to its input to a triangular waveshape.
The shape of the output waveform is determined by the size

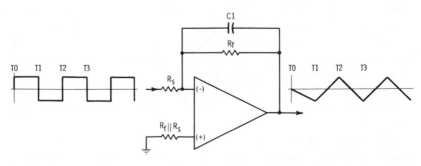

Fig. 9-7. An op amp integrator.

of the input and the values of R_s, R_f, and C1. (Resistor R_f is chosen as high as possible, consistent with maintaining enough bandwidth to handle the frequency of the input.) The circuit of Fig. 9-8 performs an operation that is the inverse of integration—differentiation. This circuit converts the input square wave into pulses, one at each transition of the input waveform.

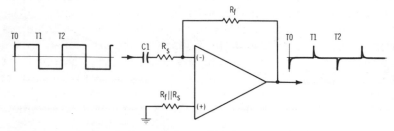

Fig. 9-8. Differentiation using the operational amplifier.

The circuit of Fig. 9-9 is a sensitive dc level detector. The output voltage is clamped at the zener voltage of diode X1 and may feed logic circuits to provide a go/no-go indication of the input signal condition. The higher the closed-loop gain of the amplifier, the greater is its sensitivity to changes in the input level. The threshold point is adjusted by varying the reference voltage, V_{ref}.

The circuits shown in the above figures are representative of the uses of the operational amplifier. They are by no means all inclusive, and there are many operational amplifier IC's. The circuit requirements will dictate the selection of an appropriate device. There are even dual op amps in a single package that lend themselves very well to applications like stereo preamplifiers. Operational amplifiers are definitely very versatile and useful devices.

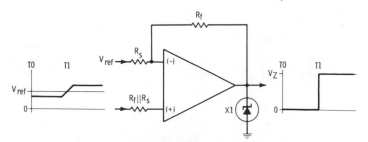

Fig. 9-9. A sensitive adjustable dc level detector.

VOLTAGE REGULATORS

Another analog IC being used more and more is the voltage regulator. It is basically an operational amplifier with a reference voltage source and a *pass transistor* added on the same substrate. The block diagram of a typical voltage-regulator IC, the μA723, is shown in Fig. 9-10. In use, the reference voltage is connected to the noninverting input (through suitable networks, as required), and the voltage to be controlled is connected to the inverting input. The operational amplifier attempts to maintain the voltage difference between the inverting and noninverting inputs at zero. Since one input is fed from a constant voltage source (V_{ref}), the result is an almost constant output voltage. Large changes in the input voltage or output current have little effect on the output voltage; the feedback through the operational amplifier keeps this voltage constant to within about 0.5 percent of V_{out} (worst case). The pass transistor raises the output-current capability above that normally associated with an operational amplifier. The current-limit terminal is normally connected to the V_{out} terminal, and a resistor is connected between the current-limit and current-sense terminals. The output is taken from the current-sense

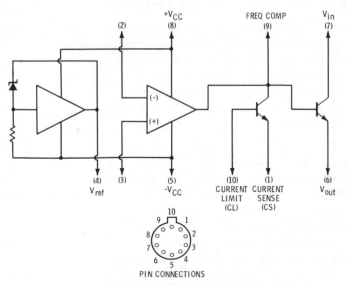

Fig. 9-10. The μA723 voltage-regulator IC.

terminal of the resistor, as shown in Fig. 9-11, the schematic of a typical low-voltage regulator ($V_{out} = 3$ to 7 volts). When the output current attempts to exceed a preset value, the voltage drop across R_s causes drive current to be removed from the pass transistor, protecting the IC from damage due to a short circuit at the output.

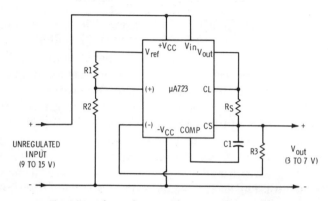

Fig. 9-11. A low-voltage regulator using the μA723.

The output voltage of the circuit of Fig. 9-11 is:

$$V_{out} = V_{ref} \frac{R2}{R1 + R2}$$

(V_{ref} for the μA723 is nominally 7.1 volts.) Resistor R3 provides compensation to prevent temperature drift of the output voltage, and it is selected to be equal to the parallel combination of R1 and R2. Capacitor C1 is the frequency compensation element and is normally 100 pF. Resistor R_s is determined from the formula $R_s = V_{limit}/I_{limit}$, where V_{limit} is the voltage required across the resistor to effect current limiting at the desired value. The magnitude of V_{limit} is normally about 0.5 and 0.8 volt.

When a μA723 is used for voltages above about 7 volts, the circuit of Fig. 9-12 is preferred. In this circuit, the signal to the inverting amplifier input rather than the signal to the noninverting input, is scaled by R1 and R2. Since the amplifier tries to maintain a zero difference between the (+) and (−) inputs, output voltages below V_{ref} require that V_{ref} be reduced, while output voltages above V_{ref} require that the output voltage be scaled down before being applied to the inverting input.

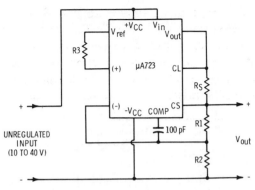

Fig. 9-12. Circuit diagram for $V_{out} = $ 7 to 35 volts.

The output voltage for the circuit of Fig. 9-12 is:

$$V_{out} = V_{ref} \frac{R1 + R2}{R2}$$

Resistor R3 is equal to R1||R2, and the total resistance R1 + R2 is normally kept below 10,000 ohms. The compensation capacitor and current-limiting resistor are the same for this circuit as for the circuit of Fig. 9-11.

The output voltage for the circuit of Fig. 9-12 is positive if the input voltage negative terminal is used for the "ground" reference and negative if the positive input terminal is used as the ground reference. If an external transistor, driven by the voltage regulator, is used as the output device, both the voltage and current handling capability of the circuit may be increased. (This is dealt with in the chapter on power supplies, Chapter 10.) For circuits requiring output voltages between 3 and 35 volts, at currents up to about 50 mA, either configuration may be adjusted to the exact value if a potentiometer is used in the resistive scaling network, as shown in Fig. 9-13.

Fig. 9-13. A variable scaling network for the voltage regulator.

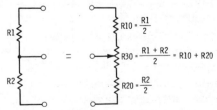

R_{total} = R1 + R2 = R10 + R20 + R30

The circuit shown in Fig. 9-14 is an af-rf signal tracer, useful for troubleshooting radios and amplifiers. The heart of the circuit is an operational amplifier, the voltage gain of which is continuously variable over the range of 1 to 100. An input diode provides demodulation for amplitude-modulated rf signals. The diode is switched out for audio-frequency signal tracing. The op amp output feeds a class-AB complementary-symmetry amplifier, which drives the speaker.

Transistors Q1 and Q2 are biased slightly on by R1-X2 and R2-X3, respectively. With low-power transistors (such as the ones shown in Fig. 9-14) that have a beta of (typically) 50, and with a 1-mA on bias, R1 and R2 $\cong$ 12 V/1 mA = 12K. Diodes X1 through X3 can be any small-signal silicon type. The 0.1-ohm resistors are placed in the emitter circuits of Q1 and Q2 to help prevent thermal runaway. To keep distortion at a minimum, the feedback signal is taken from the output of the class-AB stage, rather than from the op amp output. The op amp is connected in the noninverting input configuration to keep its input impedance high. Capacitor C1 is used to prevent any dc voltage from being applied to the op amp input.

The offset null potentiometer is adjusted to obtain zero volts across the speaker terminals with the input grounded. Variable

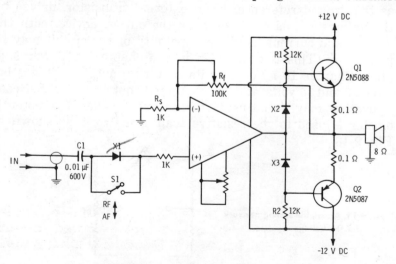

Fig. 9-14. A variable-gain af-rf signal tracer.

resistor R_f serves as the gain control, varying the amount of negative feedback around the amplifier.

Since the circuit has very high input impedance and excellent power gain, it can be used effectively in low- and high-impedance circuits at both low and high signal levels (from about 0.01 volt to about 2.8 volts peak-to-peak for a "listenable" output signal).

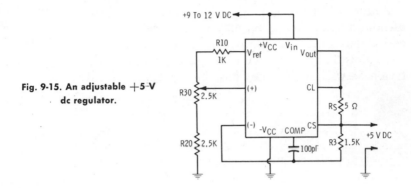

Fig. 9-15. An adjustable +5-V dc regulator.

Another practical circuit, a +5-volt regulator that can be used to supply power to digital IC's, is shown in Fig. 9-15. The total resistance of the scaling network is chosen to be about 7000 ohms to simplify the selection of R10, R20, and R30. If the circuit operation is to be +5 V at the midpoint of R30, select R1 + R2 (refer to Fig. 9-13) to equal 7000 ohms. For +5 V out, R1 should be 2000 ohms and R2 should be 5000 ohms. Make R10 = 1000 ohms, R20 = 2500 ohms, and R30 = 3500 ohms. A standard 2500-ohm potentiometer is selected for R30, since it will provide an adequate adjustment range. The value of R3 is equal to $2K\|5K \cong 1500$ ohms. (There is some error in this calculation, since the total resistance of the scaling network equals 6000 ohms rather than 7000 ohms, but it will make very little difference.)

Resistor R_s was chosen with the assumption that $V_{limit} = 0.5$ V and I_{limit} should be 100 mA. Then R_s is 0.5 V/0.1 A = 5 ohms.

The typical performance of this circuit is excellent. For input voltages between 9 to 12 volts and with load currents from 0 to 100 mA, the output will change only about 5 millivolts.

SUMMARY

Analog integrated circuits are based on the principle of the operational amplifier. Special-purpose IC's are created through modification of, or additions to, the basic op amp structure. The characteristics that an operational amplifier circuit will display are primarily dependent on external components in the feedback loop.

Analog IC's are available for almost any type of function, although some functions may cost more as a "chip" than as a collection of discrete components. The two primary advantages of analog IC's are the reduced space requirements and the relative ease with which they may be incorporated into a design.

CHAPTER 10

Power-Supply Design

There are few circuits that will operate properly from "untreated" 117-V ac 60-Hz house current, and asking batteries to provide economically the multitude of voltage and current combinations necessary in most electronic projects is simply asking too much. Where do we get the proper voltages and currents for a circuit when only house current is available? This is the function of the power supply, where the 117-V ac 60-Hz source (or any other primary power source for that matter) is converted to the various dc voltages required for the operation of a system.

The power supply is usually the last stage in a system to be designed. Even though it is usually last, its design is not the least bit less important than the design of the rest of the system. The performance of a well-designed system is no better than the performance of the system power supply. A system design adheres to the "weakest link" rule—the system is only as good as its worst stage.

DEFINING VOLTAGE AND CURRENT REQUIREMENTS

The first step in the design of a power supply is to define the output requirements. (This should sound quite familiar by now.) What voltages must be supplied to the circuitry of the system? How much current will be drawn from each output?

Are there special requirements, such as high peak-current capability, current-limiting, or protection against voltages higher than the output voltage? Each of these questions should be answered before the design of a power supply is begun.

How are the output requirements for a system power supply defined? The output voltage is usually defined by the circuitry in the system. A suitable voltage had to be selected when the circuits were originally designed. Defining the output current is a little more involved.

There are two methods that will adequately define the power-supply output current. The first is to take one-half the sum of all of the peak-to-peak currents expected to flow in all the circuits supplied from a given output and add this sum to the sum of all the quiescent currents. This total is the current that must be delivered by the power supply. The second method is a bit simpler. Use the sum of all of the maximum currents that can flow in the circuits of a system. In other words, take the currents at the $I_{C(max)}$ point on the load line of each circuit. This latter method is preferred for any digital design, since it provides adequate current when all devices are saturated. Use of the second method is also desirable for analog circuits, since it provides an extra margin on the conservative side and is simpler to calculate.

An example of this definition for a single-stage circuit is shown in Fig. 10-1. The supply current using the first method is 9 mA, while the second method yields a value of 10 mA. If more than one stage is to be supplied from the same output, the supply current is simply the sum of the stage maximum collector currents.

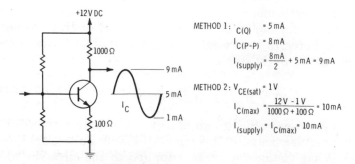

Fig. 10-1. Methods to determine power-supply output-current requirement.

Another parameter that should be specified is the *regulation* of the output voltage. The regulation defines the amount that the supply voltage can deviate from the nominal value. Changing load resistances will cause changes in the output voltage; thus, either the circuits must be designed to work properly under this changing condition or the supply must provide a stable output voltage. It should be obvious that it will be easier to regulate the supply voltage than it will be to "worst-case" design each of the circuits in a system.

If the output current is to be limited to a certain value (125 percent of nominal, for instance), this should be specified. If devices supplied from the output must be protected against voltages in excess of the nominal value, this should be specified, so that the power-supply design can incorporate the necessary circuitry.

A block diagram of a sophisticated power supply is shown in Fig. 10-2. It includes all of the features to be discussed in this chapter. These will be covered in logical order.

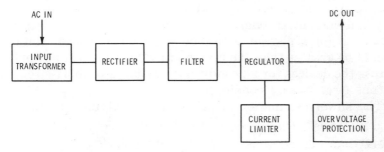

Fig. 10-2. Block diagram of a sophisticated power supply.

COMPONENT SELECTION

There are some general statements that we can make about the ratings of the components used in a power-supply design. We can then avoid having to interrupt the circuit discussions to talk about voltage, current, and power ratings.

The transformer selected for a particular design should have an rms current rating equal to or greater than the required dc output current from the supply plus the current drawn by the power-supply circuits themselves. A good rule of thumb is to add about twenty-five percent to the dc output current when selecting the transformer. Thus, a power supply that must deliver 1 amp to the ultimate load should use a transformer capable of delivering approximately 1.25 amps.

The rectifier diodes used in the supply should have a V_{BR} rating well in excess of 1.4 times the rms voltage that the transformer will impress across it. For example, a diode used with a transformer whose output is 24 V rms should have a V_{BR} rating in excess of 1.4×24 V $= 33.6$ volts. A good rule of thumb for this parameter is to add about 50 percent to the calculated V_{BR}. In this application, the actual V_{BR} should be 33.6 V $+ 0.5(33.6$ V$) = 50.4$ volts.

The diodes should have an $I_{F(max)}$ rating in excess of the output current required from the supply. Twenty percent is usually enough here, but the more margin, the better. (Remember that most diodes designed to handle more than about 3 amps usually must be heatsinked.) The rated maximum recurring peak forward current of the diodes should be greater than the peak current through them. This value can be calculated by multiplying the dc output current by a factor of 1.4.

Any transistors used should have $I_{C(max)}$ ratings twice the nominal current through them. (This is the same criteria as was used for a class-A amplifier stage.) Breakdown voltages should be greater than the maximum value that will be applied across the devices for all conditions, including a short-circuited output (worst-case) condition.

The power dissipation of all devices should also be checked at worst-case conditions. For transistors, $P_T = V_{CE(max)} \times I_{C(max)}$; for diodes, $P_T = V_{F(max)} \times I_{F(max)}$; for zener diodes, $P_T = V_Z \times I_{Z(max)}$; for resistors, $P_T = V_{max} \times I_{max}$. Most power transistors will need to be mounted on a metal plate or heat sink to allow them to dissipate safely power in excess of one-half their maximum ratings.

Lastly, capacitors should have working voltage ratings at least 15 percent higher than the highest peak voltage expected to be applied across them.

RECTIFIER CIRCUITS

There are many individual rectifier circuits, but each is either a half-wave rectifier or a full-wave rectifier. The half-wave rectifier is shown in Fig. 10-3A, and the full-wave circuit is illustrated in Fig. 10-3B. The output waveform for each

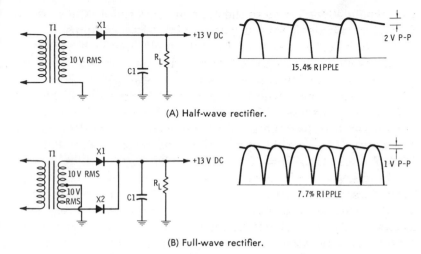

(A) Half-wave rectifier.

(B) Full-wave rectifier.

Fig. 10-3. Rectifier circuits and output waveforms.

circuit, including the "smoothing" effect of capacitor C1, is also shown. Note that the ripple frequency for the full-wave rectifier is twice that of the half-wave rectifier. The ripple voltage of the full-wave circuit (assuming equal capacitor values) is approximately half the value of a half-wave circuit, since the capacitor has less time to discharge before its voltage is replenished. For this reason, the half-wave rectifier has fallen into disuse. Most power-supply designs incorporate full-wave rectifier circuits.

The dc output voltage for each circuit is 1.4 times the rms transformer voltage applied across it less the diode drop (assumed to be 1 volt for power rectifiers). The transformer secondary winding resistance also contributes a voltage loss, but it is usually negligible. The ripple voltage is a function of C1 and R_L and is usually specified as a percentage of the total output voltage. The value of C (in microfarads) for any full-wave rectifier circuit can be found for any ripple percentage and load resistance values by using the formula:

$$C = \frac{200,000}{\dfrac{E_{out}}{I_{out}} \times \% \text{ Ripple}} \qquad \text{(Eq. 10-1)}$$

While the full-wave circuit of Fig. 10-3B is found occasionally in equipment designs, the three circuits shown in Fig.

10-4 are much more widely used. The circuit of Fig. 10-4A is a full-wave bridge rectifier. It is often used in place of the normal full-wave rectifier because it does not require a center-tapped transformer. Where two equal voltages of opposite polarity are required (such as the $+V_{CC}$ and $-V_{CC}$ for an op amp), the circuit of Fig. 10-4B may be used. This circuit is basically two full-wave rectifiers, and the transformer must be rated high enough to supply current to both R_{L1} and R_{L2}. The circuit of Fig. 10-4C provides two output voltages, one of which is twice the other. The transformer must be able to sup-

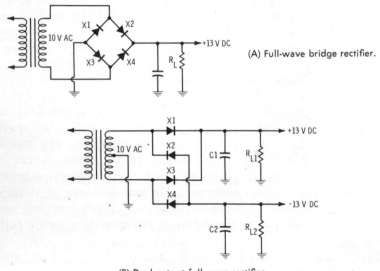

(A) Full-wave bridge rectifier.

(B) Dual-output full-wave rectifier.

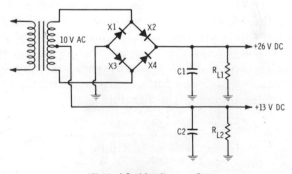

(C) Modified bridge rectifier.

Fig. 10-4. Three popular rectifier circuits.

ply the total current. Diodes X2 and X4 in Fig. 10-4C supply current only to R_{L1}, while diodes X1 and X3 must be rated for the total current through the transformer secondary. The polarity of the output voltage for the circuits of Fig. 10-4A and Fig. 10-4C may be reversed by reversing the polarity of the diodes and filter capacitors.

VOLTAGE REGULATION

While the normal rectifier circuits shown in the previous section will supply dc voltages that are adequate for many applications, they all have one serious drawback when used in systems where precise voltages are required. The output voltage will vary with changes in input voltage and output load current. This drawback is eliminated through the addition of circuitry to "regulate" the output voltage.

Fig. 10-5 shows the schematic diagram of a simple zener-diode shunt regulator circuit. It is useful for most low-power applications where only moderate control is necessary and the regulated output voltage need not be adjustable. The design of the regulator of Fig. 10-5 is quite simple. Suppose that a +10-V collector-voltage supply is required to feed a three-stage amplifier whose total current drain varies from 10 to 50 milli-amps. This corresponds to a maximum power requirement of 0.5 watt. The zener diode should have a P_T rating at least twice this value, or 1 watt. For the zener to remain in the breakdown mode, the voltage at point A in Fig. 10-5 should never go below about 130 percent of the zener voltage, and the voltage at the cathode of the zener must never go below the zener voltage. For this circuit, we need at least 13 volts at point A when the input voltage is at minimum; add a volt for the diode drop and multiply by 0.707. This gives us the minimum rms secondary voltage required, (13 V + 1 V) × 0.707 =

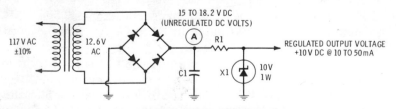

Fig. 10-5. A simple zener-diode shunt regulator.

10 V ac, so the transformer, at nominal line-voltage input (117 V ac) should have a secondary voltage of about 11 V ac. A standard 12.6-V filament transformer will be adequate. Now calculate the actual minimum and maximum voltages at point A. Minimum is $(12.6 \times 1.4) - 0.1 (12.6 \times 1.4) - 1 V \cong 15$ V dc, and maximum is $(12.6 \times 1.4) + 0.1 (12.6 \times 1.4) - 1 V \cong 18.2$ V dc. These voltages and the minimum and maximum load currents allow us to specify R1 and insure that overdissipation in X1 will not occur.

The maximum value for R1 is the value that will drop $V_{A(min)}$ (the minimum voltage at point A) minus V_{out} at a current of $I_{out(max)} + I_{Z(min)}$. Current $I_{Z(min)}$ is usually chosen to be about 10 percent of the maximum allowable zener current, so for a 10-V, 1-watt zener, $I_{Z(max)} = 1$ W/10 V = 100 mA, and $I_{Z(min)}$ is therefore chosen to be 10 mA. The value of R1 is found by using the formula:

$$R = \frac{V_{A(min)} - V_{out}}{I_{out} + I_{Z(min)}} \qquad \text{(Eq. 10-2)}$$

For the circuit of Fig. 10-5, R1 = (15 V − 10V)/(50 mA + 10 mA) = 5 V/60 mA = 83.3 ohms. Remembering that this is the maximum value, choose R1 as the next lowest standard value, 82 ohms.

Zener dissipation is checked at the condition of maximum voltage at point A and minimum output current. With 18.2 V − 10 V across it, R1 draws 8.2 V/82 ohms = 100 mA. About 10 mA of this current goes to the load, so the dissipation is 90 mA × 10 V = 0.9 W, only slightly below the diode maximum rating. (For the sake of completeness, the normal dissipation, assuming nominal voltage and a 30-mA load, may be computed as follows. The nominal voltage at point A is $(12.6 \times 1.4) - 1 = 16.6$ V. Then the voltage across R1 is 16.6 − 10 = 6.6 V. The total current is 6.6 V/82 ohms = 80.5 mA. Since the load current is 30 mA, the diode current is 80.5 − 30 = 50.5 mA, and P_T is therefore 10 V × 50.5 mA = 505 mW = 0.505 watt.) The maximum power dissipated in R1 is $(I_{max})^2 R = 0.82$ watt, so a 2-W resistor should be used.

If the range of input voltage and output current can be restricted, the value of R1 can be increased, but the nature of this circuit restricts its usefulness to low-power applications if the components are to have a safe, long life. If it is neces-

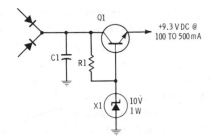

Fig. 10-6. A zener-diode-stabilized
series regulator.

+9.3 V DC @
100 TO 500 mA

sary to regulate the output voltage of a circuit at higher output current levels, the circuit of Fig. 10-6 can be used. This circuit takes advantage of the beta of the series transistor, Q1, to increase the output current range. Resistor R1 and zener diode X1 now regulate the voltage at the base of Q1, and the relatively constant V_{BE} of Q1 does not affect the regulation. If the beta of Q1 is 10, the output current can vary from 100 mA to 500 mA.

Note that the V_{BE} of Q1 must be subtracted from the zener voltage when the output voltage is calculated. Minor adjustments may be made to the output voltage by adding a diode in series with either the zener or the transistor to increase or decrease the output voltage. This is illustrated in Fig. 10-7. The design of the zener portion of this type of circuit is the same as the design of the simple circuit. Just use the output current values divided by the beta of the transistor to calculate the size of R1. Any of these circuits can be designed for a range of zero to the maximum allowable current, if zero is used as the minimum output current in the previous equations. Then the zener dissipates $(V_Z \times I_{out(max)})/\beta$ under no-load conditions.

Remember to select a transistor with suitable characteristics. For the circuit of Fig. 10-6, Q1 should have the follow-

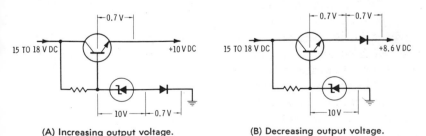

(A) Increasing output voltage.

(B) Decreasing output voltage.

Fig. 10-7. Diodes used for output voltage trimming.

ing rating: $V_{BR(CBO)} > 8.2$ V, $V_{BR(CEO)} > 8.9$ V, $I_{C(max)} > 500$ mA, $I_{B(max)} > 50$ mA, beta $\cong 10$, and $P_T > 4.45$ W. These are absolute minimum requirements, and they assume that the load is never going to be shorted. If the load should become a short circuit, the following voltages, currents, and power dissipations are present in the circuit of Fig. 10-6: V_{CE} becomes 18.2 V, V_{CB} becomes 17.5 volts (assuming $V_{BE} = 0.7$ V), I_C goes to about 2.3 amps, I_B is 230 mA, and P_T becomes 42 watts (almost ten times its normal value). These are some of the reasons why every parameter in the design of a power supply should be checked thoroughly. Some ways to prevent destruction of the components in a regulator circuit will be developed in the section on protective circuits.

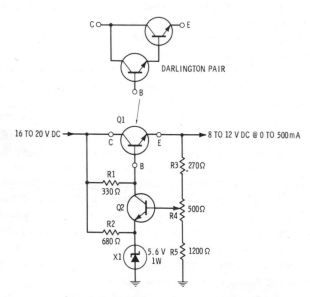

Fig. 10-8. A feedback-amplifier series regulator.

When it is necessary to have an adjustable output or an output with better regulation than the simple zener-regulated circuits shown so far, the circuit of Fig. 10-8 works well. It uses the zener diode as a reference voltage and compares a sample of the output voltage with the reference voltage. The circuit is, in essence, a differential amplifier with a large amount of negative feedback. This feedback compensates for variations in V_Z and V_{BE} for changing load currents, lowers the output impedance of the supply, and reduces the ripple and noise present at its output.

The design, while more complex than that previously required, is relatively straightforward. Diode X1 should have a zener voltage approximately one-half the value of the output voltage (± 50 percent as there is plenty of leeway here). Resistor R2 should supply about $0.1\ I_{Z(max)}$ to X1. Resistor R1 supplies base current to Q1 and should be calculated at $V_{in(min)}$ and $I_{out(max)}$ conditions. Transistor Q2 and diode X1 sink current away from the base of Q1 during the regulation process, so they should be rated accordingly. For high current outputs, a Darlington-pair transistor or two transistors in a Darlington configuration can be used in place of Q1. This reduces the current variations through Q2 and X1 and helps to keep their power dissipation low.

The voltage divider consisting of R3, R4, and R5 should draw about one percent of the maximum output current required of the supply. The individual values of these resistors are selected in the following manner. Resistor R5 should drop V_Z plus V_{BE}, so that the base current of Q2 never goes to zero. Resistor R3 limits the base current through Q2 to a safe value, and R4, which determines the adjustment range, is $R_{total} - R3 - R5$. There is also some latitude in the selection of these values to permit the use of standard-value components.

An example should illustrate the procedure. The desired output is 8 to 12 V dc at currents from 0 to 500 mA. Diode X1 is chosen first. We will use a standard 5.6-V, 1-watt zener whose $I_{Z(max)}$ is 178 mA, so R2 should drop 10.4 V at 15 mA (15 mA $\cong$ $0.1\ I_{Z(max)}$). Therefore, $R2 = 10.4\ V/15\ mA = 693$ ohms, rounded off to a standard 680-ohm unit. If Q1 has a beta of 50 and R1 must supply 10 mA with 3.3 V dropped across it (16 V $-$ 12.7 V), its value should be 3.3 V/10 mA = 330 ohms. If we assume the nominal V_{out} to be 10 V dc, the divider network should total 10 V/(0.01)(500 mA) = 2000 ohms. A nominal 5 mA will flow through R3, R4, and R5.

The voltage that should be dropped across R5 is 5.6 V + 0.7 V = 6.3 V, so its value is 6.3 V/5 mA = 1260 ohms. Choose the nearest standard value, 1200 ohms. When $V_{in} = 20$ V dc, $V_{out} = 8$ V dc, and $I_{out} = 0$ mA, then the maximum collector current through Q2 is 34 mA. If the beta of Q2 equals 100, 0.34 mA of base current will be required. The voltage at the base of Q2 should not be allowed to exceed V_Z plus about 1 volt, so at this condition, R3 should drop $8 - 6.6 = 1.4$ volts. Since the 5-mA divider current is far greater than the maximum I_B required by Q2, use it to calculate R3. Then $R3 = 1.4\ V/5\ mA = 280$ ohms; a standard value of 270 ohms will suffice. The value of R4 is then $2000 - 1200 - 270 = 530$ ohms. A 500-ohm potentiometer should work well.

This completes the design except for the calculation of all rating requirements and the selection of the transistors. Final adjustments may still have to be made on the bench, but the circuit should function.

Two of the other voltage-regulator circuit configurations are the shunt regulator and the series regulator using an IC as the control amplifier for the series *pass transistor*. The shunt regulator has fallen into disuse, since it usually consumes more power than other circuits. The discussion of the IC regulator is left to the practical circuits section of this chapter, so that the protective circuits incorporated in it may be discussed first.

CURRENT REGULATION

The constant-current sources discussed in Chapter 5 can be augmented through the use of suitable amplifier transistors to increase their effective output ranges. One such circuit is shown in Fig. 10-9. The FET, acting as a constant-current source for the base of Q2, maintains the collector current of Q2 at a constant value of $(\beta + 1)\,I_B$. Resistor R2 in the circuit is used to bypass and I_{CBO} to the emitter of Q2, and it should draw about 0.1 I_B at the selected output current.

A feedback-controlled current regulator, configured along the same general lines as the series pass voltage regulator, is much more versatile than the simple constant-current source of Fig. 10-9. Its circuit is shown in Fig. 10-10. In this circuit, the reference voltage is compared against the voltage across a current-monitoring resistor (R_M), rather than across the output of the supply.

A standard silicon diode is used as the reference source to keep the value of R_M relatively low. When the output current tries to decrease, the drop across R_M decreases, and less base current is fed to Q2. The collector voltage of Q2 rises, supplying more current to Q1 and raising the output voltage in

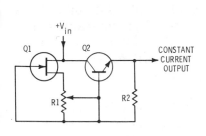

Fig. 10-9. A FET-controlled high-level
constant-current source.

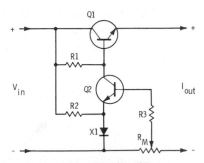

Fig. 10-10. An adjustable
current regulator.

an attempt to keep the current constant. This action tends to keep the output current constant at the set point, regardless of the load resistance attached to the supply.

The calculation of R1 and R2 is similar to that for the corresponding resistors in a constant-voltage supply. Resistor R_M must be chosen so that a minimum of about 0.7 V is dropped across it at the minimum required output current. Resistor R3 limits the base current of Q2 to a safe level.

PROTECTIVE CIRCUITS

Protective circuits for power supplies take two basic forms— overvoltage protection and overcurrent protection. Overvoltage protection may be used where a voltage higher than the supply voltage can be accidentally applied to the supply output, resulting in possible damage to the supply and the circuits it is connected to. Overcurrent protection is aimed primarily at protecting the power-supply components. Both are quite simple to implement.

One of the simplest overvoltage protection circuits is shown in Fig. 10-11. It is simply an adjustable level detector using an SCR to clamp the power-supply output at (effectively) zero volts when an overvoltage condition is detected. It can be reset by removing the input power to the supply. If it is desired, a second SCR (X3 in Fig. 10-11) can be added to trip the input circuit breaker when an overvoltage condition occurs, preventing overdissipation of the regulator components.

To add current limiting to a series regulator, the circuit of Fig. 10-12 may be used. Note that it is a circuit similar to the

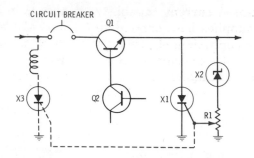

Fig. 10-11. An SCR overvoltage-protection circuit.

current regulator previously discussed. When the output current exceeds a preset value, transistor Q3 turns on, robbing transistor Q1 of base drive and reducing the output current to a safe level. Resistor R_M determines the minimum current value at which the supply will limit, and the potentiometer allows adjustment from minimum to infinity. Resistor R_M should drop about 0.7 V at I_{min} and will usually be a high-wattage, low-value unit, since it carries the full load current (the shunting effect of R6 is negligible).

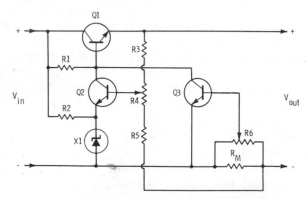

Fig. 10-12. Overcurrent protection with a series regulator.

PRACTICAL CIRCUITS

The voltage-regulator IC discussed in Chapter 9 incorporates many of the features of the voltage regulators discussed in this chapter and forms the basis for a versatile variable-output power supply with current-limiting protection. The circuit, using a μA723 IC feeding an external series pass transistor for increased current capability, is shown in Fig. 10-13. The µA723 supplies base current to Q1, and the emitter current of Q1 is approximately beta times the IC output current. Resistor R1 senses the current being delivered to the load and limits it to approximately 1.3 amps under short-circuit conditions. The divider network is chosen to equal 10K (R2 + R3 + R4), and the individual values are selected in the same way

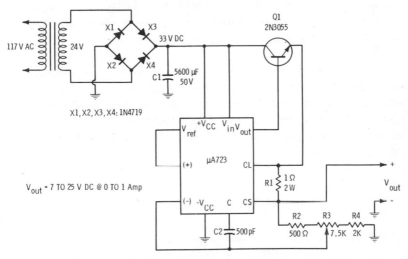

Fig. 10-13. An IC voltage-regulated, current-limited power supply.

they were for the discrete series-regulator circuit. Note that the (−) input is connected to the emitter of Q1 rather than to the output of the IC, so variations caused by temperature and voltage changes within the transistor are also nulled out. Do not forget the compensating capacitor, C2. The 1N4719 diodes are rated at 3 amps, and capacitor C1 is calculated to provide about one-percent ripple at a one-amp load current. The ripple at the output of the supply is, of course, much lower.

This power-supply circuit should prove extremely useful for anyone designing or tinkering with solid-state circuits.

SUMMARY

The power supply is an important part of a system design. Some systems require only "bulk" voltages from simple regulators. Others need more precise voltage regulation.

There are many circuit variations for obtaining voltage regulation, ranging from the simple zener-diode shunt regulator to the IC-driven, current-limited, series pass-transistor regulator. Current-regulated power supplies may be developed by choosing the proper sensing point in a standard circuit design.

Protective circuits for overvoltage and overcurrent conditions prevent accidental destruction of regulator components and circuitry due to exceeding the breakdown-voltage or power-dissipation limits.

Index